Like many things recently, your *National Trust Handbook* has had to change a little. This year we will have the vast majority of places open and ready for you to enjoy. Even in the event of further lockdowns, there will still be parks, gardens and coastal and countryside sites there for you. But Covid restrictions mean that some places will sometimes be unable to open safely. We didn't want to give you inaccurate information, so we haven't included opening times or information on cafés and shops in the handbook this year.

Please do continue to check **nationaltrust.org.uk** to plan your visit, or call us on **0344 800 1895**. That way you can be confident about what's open and when, before you set off.

This handbook will provide you with all the inspiration you need to choose your next visit and learn more about the places we look after. Without your support we simply could not continue to care for them – thank you.

See the next page for what's had to go online, and what's still in the handbook.

For everyone, for ever.

I hope you feel reassured by that simple, powerful promise. The Trust – and all the places we care for – have faced tough times before, from disease and depression to world wars. Yet we're still here, caring for nature, beauty and history in this ever-changing world.

It's been a year of adaptation and change, and for us that's included changing the *National Trust Handbook*. It has changed throughout its history and this edition retains all the inspiration you need to choose where you would like to visit, but doesn't include details that could become inaccurate or misleading.

Our handbook may have changed, but the places in our care haven't and nor has the importance of nature, beauty and history in our lives.

Without your support we wouldn't be able to continue to look after these places for future generations to enjoy, so on behalf of all of us at the National Trust, thank you.

Hilary McGrady
Director-General

What's in your handbook?

- Who we are and what we do

- Descriptions and photographs of places we look after

- How to contact them and visit them

- Maps showing all these places

- Introductions to Historic House Hotels and National Trust Partners

To view a personal video message to members, go to: **nationaltrust.org.uk/ handbook-welcome**

Trelissick, Cornwall

What's online?

- Opening dates and times, prices, and all transient details
- Access information
- Things to see and do
- Eating, drinking and shopping
- Dogs – where they're welcome, and where there are restrictions
- Holiday cottages, hotels, bothies and campsites
- Our 'Land Map' – everything looked after by the Trust
- How to get more involved

And the best ways to get to it:

1. **National Trust website**
   Browse specific web pages for the place you want to visit

2. **National Trust app**
   For all the up-to-date details on your phone – scan this QR code to download the app now

If you'd prefer not to go online, or it's tricky to do so where you are, call 0344 800 1895.

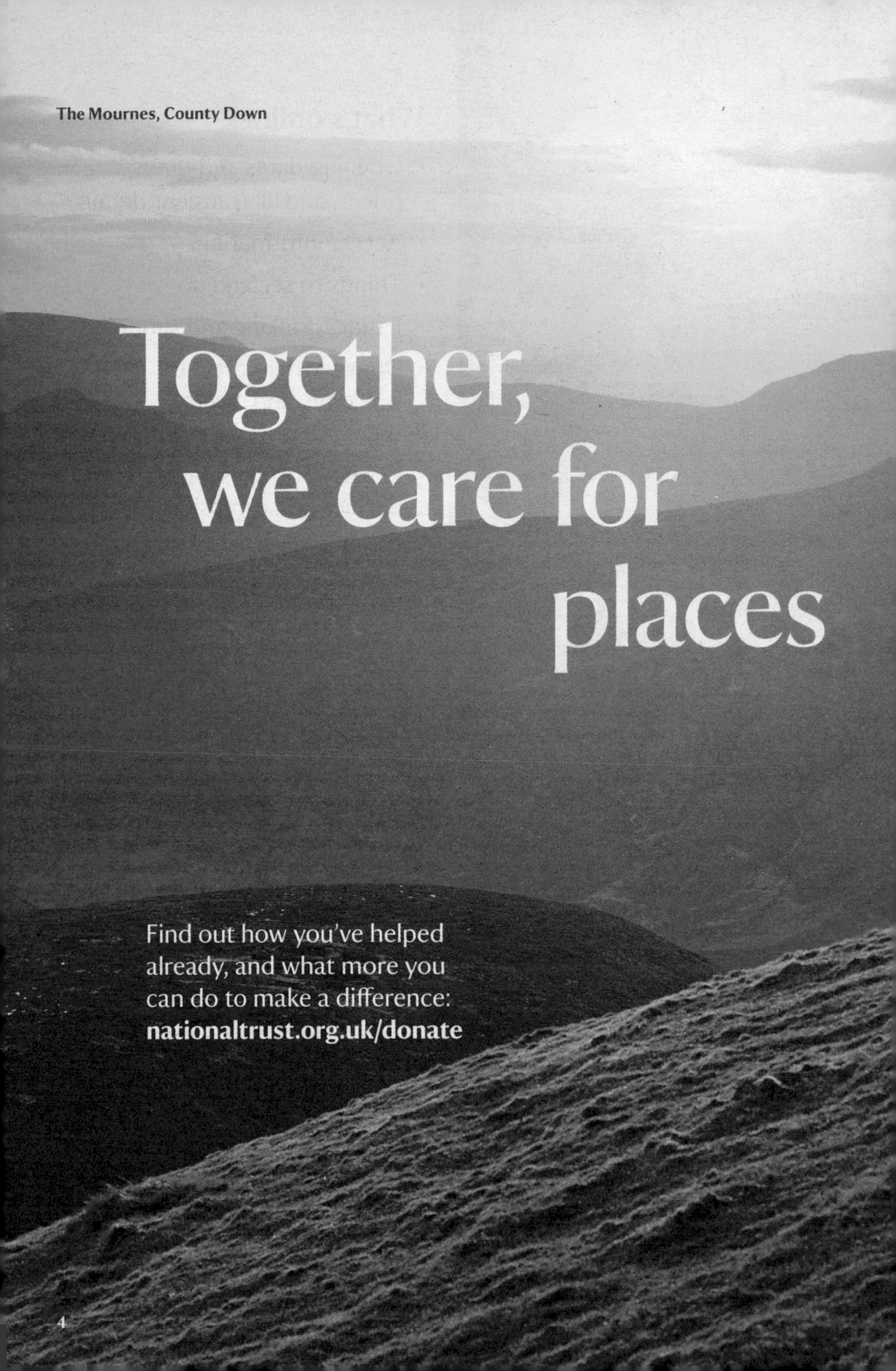
The Mournes, County Down
Together, we care for places
Find out how you've helped already, and what more you can do to make a difference:
nationaltrust.org.uk/donate

so that

people
and nature
can thrive.

Thank you for joining Europe's
biggest conservation charity.
Thank you for getting involved,
thank you for making a difference.

Who we are

In 1895,

three far-sighted people founded the National Trust on the belief that everyone has a deep human need for nature, beauty and history. It's what connects us all and enables us to thrive.

Robert Hunter

Octavia Hill

Hardwicke Rawnsley

Discover more about their lives and their legacy:
nationaltrust.org.uk/our-founders

Thanks to you, and to the
generations of members
who've gone before you,
we now look after:

- **hundreds of
  miles of coast**

- **thousands of acres of
  countryside, woods,
  parks and gardens**

- **and the precious
  houses, industrial
  buildings, artefacts
  and collections that
  tell our national history**

And we're entrusted by law
to protect all of it for ever.

Together, our purpose is to protect and care for...

nature

Everyone needs nature

And recently, people everywhere have felt this need – hearing, seeing and sensing nature as though for the first time. It spells hope.

Everyone needs that deep nourishment of green spaces and fresh air.

But nature needs our help. Climate change threatens wildlife and the balance of the natural world – all that we hold dear, and require to live well. Together with others, we must take action now.

Find out about our plans for tackling climate change at **nationaltrust.org.uk/ climate-change**

Derwent Water, Cumbria

beauty

'We all want quiet. We all want beauty … we all need space. Unless we have it, we cannot reach that sense of quiet in which whispers of better things come to us gently.'

Octavia Hill, 1883.

history

Thanks to you, we will keep on caring for historic places.

And we'll make sure that future generations can still get to see them, walk through them, feel their atmosphere, learn from them, wonder at them, simply enjoy them –

all the grand **houses,** the long-tended **gardens** and **landscapes,** the collections of **art** and personal **treasures,** the **mills** and **mines** and ruined **castles,** the mysterious **ancient sites**, and people's **homes** that are like precious **time capsules**.

It's all about **connecting** with the past,

sensing it.

Sparking the imagination.

Doesn't everyone love a bit of time travel?

Discover the collections we look after, and all the rich and complex stories they have to tell us: **nationaltrust.org.uk/art-and-collections**

for everyone

When we say 'for everyone', we mean it.

We believe, as did our founders, that nature, beauty and history are for everyone.

We all have a part to play in making everyone feel welcome.

Help us make sure that the National Trust – and all the places we look after on behalf of the whole nation – is a safe and supportive environment for all people, where visible and invisible differences are respected and valued.

Everyone can get involved, everyone can make a difference.

for ever

**When we say 'for ever',
we mean it.**

'For ever' means that through wars, pandemics, recessions and all our darkest times, the National Trust has still been here, caring for the places that people love. And we have to adapt and respond to what people most need from us in changing times.

The founders of the Trust knew that the only way to protect precious places for ever – and people's access to them – was to own them. And they had the foresight to guarantee this 'for ever' ownership through a crucial Act of Parliament in 1907.

Your membership will carry on making a difference to people's lives far into the future.

We're committed to improving access everywhere, but every place is different. Find out more here:
nationaltrust.org.uk/access

You and your Trust

Don't miss out

There's lots going on that you won't get to hear about unless we can contact you. Register with **My National Trust** and you can:

- **choose** how you want to hear from us,

- **choose** what you'd like to hear about,

- **update** your contact details and preferred ways to pay,

- **keep** a list of all your favourite places.

And did you know? If you share your membership with others, they can register their choices too.

nationaltrust.org.uk/mynt

My National Trust

Welcome

Account
Edit your settings.
Email Supporter@emailaddress.co.uk

See your account details >

Memberships
Manage your memberships including gift ones.
Your own membership

Sugar Loaf,
Monmouthshire

More for members

Have you found your dedicated **members' area** on the website? Here you'll find previews, videos and behind-the-scenes stories. And you'll be first to see new features on the website, such as:

- seasonal recipes from our chefs' kitchens, and 'what's in season?' food advice

- tips from our gardeners, wildlife experts and curators

- ideas for family activities

- spotlights on collections, conservation work and recent discoveries

- upcoming shop and holiday offers, and member events

- the most up-to-date visiting announcements

nationaltrust.org.uk/ members-area

How else can you stay in touch? Keep an eye on our social media channels and podcasts, and opt in for emails on My National Trust.

Freshly picked at Felbrigg Hall, Norfolk

Data protection – our promise to you

We have to store your data to keep in touch with you, but we promise we'll keep your details safe and never send you anything that you haven't agreed to receive. And we promise we'll never sell your personal data to third parties.

You can change your mind at any time – about how you want to hear from us or what you want to hear about – by going to **nationaltrust.org.uk/mynt** or by calling **0344 800 1895**.

Did you know?

There are three historic houses – in North Wales, North Yorkshire and Buckinghamshire – where you can go and stay the night, with all profits going to the Trust to fund our conservation work. If you've ever dreamt of sleeping in a National Trust house, then read on.

Historic House Hotels Ltd was founded in 1979 to rescue and restore run-down country houses, and give them a new life as hotels. In 2008 the hotels were given to us to ensure their long-term protection.

Each has its own character and atmosphere. But all three share that feeling of staying in a private country house, with the smell of woodsmoke from open fires, grand sweeping staircases, trays of afternoon tea and beautiful gardens to stroll through in the evening.

Middlethorpe Hall, just outside York

Bodysgallen Hall, near Llandudno

Hartwell House, Buckinghamshire

Afternoon tea at Hartwell House

To find out more, have a look at the hotels' main entries on pages 119, 326 and 353, or visit **historichousehotels.com**

Planning your visit

Between pages 20 and 411 you'll find individual entries for places we care for throughout England, Wales and Northern Ireland.

All the changeable details to do with visiting these places – their opening dates and times, prices, facilities, events, dog access and so on – are now held online to make sure they're always up-to-date. See page 3 for the best ways to get to this information. And you can always call **0344 800 1895** if you can't get online.

Getting there

Each place entry includes its address, contact details and a postcode for satnavs. If this misdirects, we include a warning or directions. Locations are shown on maps in each chapter.

And not just by car

Many places are easy to get to by train, bus, walking or cycling. Check our website for details of the place you want to visit, or use **traveline.info** (England and Wales) or **translink.co.uk** (Northern Ireland) for public transport, and **sustrans.org.uk** for cycle routes.

If you'd like a free copy of our **Getting Here Guide** – with maps, directions and details of public transport, cycling and walking routes – call **0344 800 1895**, or go to **nationaltrust.org.uk/ gettinghere** to download a pdf.

We also print an **Access Guide**, showing which facilities we have at which places, such as powered mobility vehicles, and 'Changing Places' or 'Space To Change' toilets. Download a pdf from **nationaltrust.org.uk/access** or call **0344 800 1895** for a printed copy.

We're working towards every place featured in the handbook having its own access statement on the website.

What kind of place is it?

The symbols at the start of each place entry tell you something about what you'll find there – see the key (right). There are more details on the website and app.

Each place entry also contains **access symbols**, and the key for them is on the inside back cover.

Places key

 Historic house

 Castle/fort

 Church/chapel

 Watermill

 Windmill

 Other buildings

 Archaeological site

 Farm/farm animals

 Garden

 Countryside/park

 Coast

 Nature reserve

1947

Why the date? This gives you the year that a place came into the care of the Trust. You can find more details on **ntlandmap.org.uk**

Cornwall

Walking a clifftop path at
The Rumps, Pentire

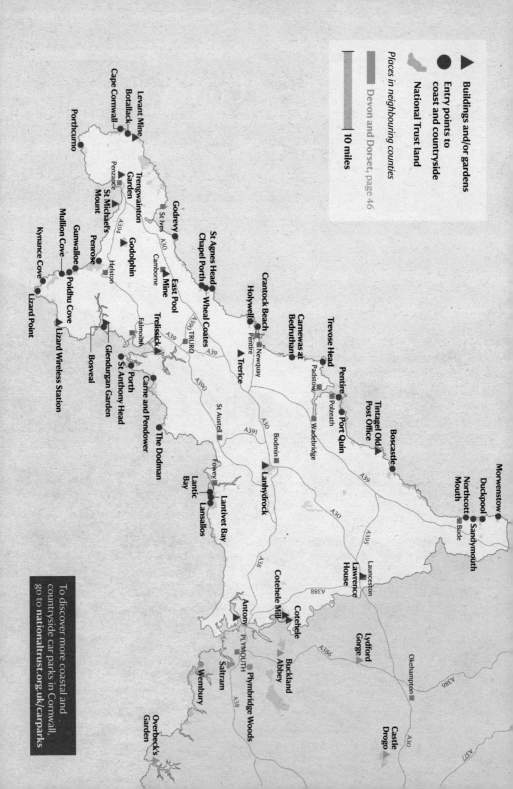

Antony

Torpoint, Cornwall PL11 2QA

`1961` 🏛️ ✤

Centuries-old portraits preside over glimpses of present-day life in this house full of personal treasures, which is still lived in today by the Carew Pole family. Playful topiary, a cone-shaped fountain and intriguing sculptures accompany sweeping views in the garden. Antony is a great place to lose track of time.

Access: 🅿️ 🅳 🚽 🚶 ♿

Find out more: 01752 812191 or antony@nationaltrust.org.uk
nationaltrust.org.uk/antony

A lavender-lined path at Antony, below, and centuries-old portraits, bottom

Boscastle

near Tintagel, Cornwall

`1955` 🛥️ 🏛️

The snaking entrance to Boscastle's harbour

There has been a fishing and trading port here for centuries, with boats coming and going between the high cliffs that guard the snaking harbour entrance. Much of Boscastle can be discovered on foot, with footpaths leading in all directions. You can walk in the footsteps of the young Thomas Hardy through the wildlife-rich ancient woodland in the Valency Valley, or explore the rare medieval field system known as 'the Forrabury Stitches' high above the village. The striking lookout building on Willapark headland, and the historic churches of Minster and Forrabury, are nearby.

The wildlife-rich Valency Valley offers walks through ancient woodland

Note: toilet by main car park (not National Trust). **Satnav**: use PL35 0HD.

Access: 🚻♿

Find out more: 01840 250010 or boscastle@nationaltrust.org.uk
nationaltrust.org.uk/boscastle

Bosveal

near Mawnan Smith,
Falmouth, Cornwall 1980

Walks from here take in wooded valleys, secluded coves and soft, sheltered shores of the Helford River and Falmouth Bay.
Note: toilets at nearby Glendurgan Garden. Holiday cottages at Bosloe and Durgan.
Satnav: use TR11 5JR.

Find out more: 01326 252020 or bosveal@nationaltrust.org.uk
nationaltrust.org.uk/bosveal

Botallack

on the Tin Coast, near St Just, Cornwall

1995 🚻🏛♿🖼

On the wild Tin Coast, the famed Crowns engine houses cling to the foot of the cliffs in a landscape transformed by its industrial past. From here Cornish miners changed the world, and today it's part of the Cornish Mining World Heritage Site.
Note: industrial landscape with mine shafts and exposed cliffs – please keep to paths.
Satnav: use TR19 7QQ. Beware, some satnavs misdirect. Keep to the B3306 until you reach Botallack village.

Access: 🅿♿🚻♿♿

Find out more: 01736 786934 or botallack@nationaltrust.org.uk
nationaltrust.org.uk/botallack

Remains of mine buildings at Botallack on the Tin Coast

Cape Cornwall

on the Tin Coast, near St Just, Cornwall

1987

Cape Cornwall and the Kenidjack Valley

The distinctive headland of Cape Cornwall juts out into the ocean where two great bodies of water meet. Once a heavily industrialised landscape, it is now part of the Cornish Mining World Heritage Site, and a wild and rugged home to the many seabirds that nest on the Brisons Rocks. **Note**: narrow lanes, unsuitable for caravans. Industrial landscape – please keep to paths for your own safety. **Satnav**: use TR19 7NN for Cape Cornwall car park. Beware some satnavs misdirect. Follow the signs in St Just town to Cape Cornwall.

Access: 🔣

Find out more: 01736 786934 or capecornwall@nationaltrust.org.uk
nationaltrust.org.uk/cape-cornwall

Carne and Pendower

near Veryan, Cornwall

1961

Two of the best beaches on the Roseland peninsula: fine stretches of sand and rock pools, popular with families. Walks along the coast and inland reveal the area's wildlife – great for butterflies in summer and birds in winter. Lots of history to discover nearby, from Bronze Age to Cold War. **Note**: seasonal toilets in both car parks. **Satnav**: for Carne use TR2 5PF; Pendower TR2 5PF (turn right at sign for Pendower Beach).

Find out more: 01872 501062 or carne@nationaltrust.org.uk
nationaltrust.org.uk/carne-and-pendower

Pendower Beach on the Roseland peninsula

Carnewas at Bedruthan

near Padstow, Cornwall

1930

Since Victorian times this has been one of the most popular destinations on the Cornish coast, known for its spectacular clifftop views of giant rock stacks striding across Bedruthan Beach (not National Trust). For a longer walk, follow the coast path to Park Head and the sheltered cove of Porth Mear beyond. Carpets of spring and autumn squill bedeck these clifftops, and birds nesting from March include linnets, stonechats and skylarks.
Note: no beach access and unsafe to enter the sea at any time. **Satnav**: use PL27 7UW.

Access:

Find out more: 01637 860563 or carnewas@nationaltrust.org.uk
nationaltrust.org.uk/carnewas-at-bedruthan

Carnewas at Bedruthan

Chapel Porth

near St Agnes, Cornwall

1957

The beach at Chapel Porth at low tide

At the foot of a steep valley between high heathery cliffs, Chapel Porth Beach is a shingle strip at high tide and a huge expanse of sand at low tide. The area is steeped in mining history, with many remains to be discovered on walks.
Note: seasonal toilets. Take care not to get cut off by incoming tide. Seasonal lifeguards. **Satnav**: use TR5 0NS.

Access:

Find out more: 01872 552412 or chapelporth@nationaltrust.org.uk
nationaltrust.org.uk/chapel-porth

Cotehele

St Dominick, near Saltash,
Cornwall PL12 6TA

1947

This rambling granite and slate-stone home, high above the River Tamar, was built by the Edgcumbes and remained in their family for nearly 600 years. Time has stood still. The hall, with its ancient timber roof and displays of weaponry, and the warren of tapestry-clad rooms beyond have changed little since Tudor times. The 5-hectare (12-acre) garden features historic daffodils, terraces, ponds and orchards with 150 local apple varieties. The Valley Garden,

Little has changed since Tudor times at Cotehele, below and right

Cotehele Mill

St Dominick, near Saltash,
Cornwall PL12 6TA

1947

**Restored 19th-century
Cotehele Mill, above and below**

A peaceful walk alongside the Morden
stream from Cotehele Quay takes you to
the restored 19th-century Cotehele Mill.
Traditional woodworker and potter
on site, as well as recreated wheelwright's,
saddler's and blacksmith's workshops.
Note: nearest toilets at Cotehele Quay.

Access:

Find out more: 01579 350606 (mill).
01579 351346 (Cotehele) or
cotehele@nationaltrust.org.uk
nationaltrust.org.uk/cotehele-mill

**Visitors explore the garden, top, and discover
displays of weaponry, above, at Cotehele**

with medieval stewpond and dovecote,
leads to Cotehele Quay – thriving in
Victorian times – where you'll find the 1899
Tamar sailing barge *Shamrock*, lime kilns
and Discovery Centre. **Note**: the house has
no electricity, so feel free to bring a torch.
Satnav: follow to St Mellion or St Ann's
Chapel, then follow signs.

Access:

Find out more: 01579 351346 or
cotehele@nationaltrust.org.uk
nationaltrust.org.uk/cotehele

Crantock Beach

near Newquay, Cornwall

1956

Close to Newquay, this feels like a different Cornwall: Crantock Beach (above) is an expanse of golden sand, great for sandcastles and surfing. Wonderful walking country – through the dunes on Rushy Green, along the banks of the Gannel Estuary, or around the headland of West Pentire. **Note**: danger, unpredictable currents and sheer drops from dunes. **Satnav**: use TR8 5RN for Crantock Beach and TR8 5QS for Treago Mill.

Access:

Find out more: 01208 863046 or crantockbeach@nationaltrust.org.uk
nationaltrust.org.uk/crantock-beach

The Dodman

Penare, near Gorran Haven, Cornwall 1919

The highest headland on Cornwall's south coast, with massive Iron Age ramparts. Great walking, wildlife and beaches. **Note**: footpaths to Hemmick Beach and Dodman Point. **Satnav**: use PL26 6NY – go past Treveague Farm and continue down hill.

Find out more: 01872 501062 or thedodman@nationaltrust.org.uk
nationaltrust.org.uk/the-dodman

Duckpool

near Bude, Cornwall 1960

Remote beach with rock pools at the mouth of the wooded Coombe Valley, overlooked by cliffs carpeted with wild flowers. **Note**: toilets open seasonally. **Satnav**: use EX23 9JN.

Find out more: 01208 863046 or duckpool@nationaltrust.org.uk
nationaltrust.org.uk/duckpool

East Pool Mine

near Redruth, Cornwall

1967

East Pool celebrates the extraordinary lives of people who worked at the very heart of what is now the Cornish Mining World Heritage Site. With two giant beam engines, preserved in towering engine houses, this is a place for all the family to discover the dramatic story of Cornish mining. **Satnav**: for main site, use TR15 3NH; for Trevithick Cottage use TR14 0QG.

Access:

Find out more: 01209 315027 or eastpool@nationaltrust.org.uk
Trevithick Road, Pool, Cornwall TR15 3NP
nationaltrust.org.uk/east-pool-mine

Discovering the story of Cornish mining at East Pool Mine

The puzzling maze at Glendurgan Garden

Glendurgan Garden

Mawnan Smith, near Falmouth,
Cornwall TR11 5JZ

1962 🏠 ❀ ♿ ⛰

Glendurgan Garden was described by its
creators, the Quakers Alfred and Sarah Fox,
as a 'small peace [sic] of heaven on earth'.
Visitors can find out why it proved to be
just this for the Foxes and their 12 children
by exploring Glendurgan's three valleys,
running down to the sheltered beach at
Durgan on the Helford River. There's a
puzzling maze, created by Alfred and
Sarah to entertain the family. You can
enjoy camellias, magnolias and primroses
in early spring, then rhododendrons and
bluebells in May, followed by the exotic
greens of summer and dramatic autumn
colour in the trees. **Note**: steep paths,
steps, uneven terrain.

Access: ♿ ♿

Find out more: 01326 252020 or
glendurgan@nationaltrust.org.uk
nationaltrust.org.uk/glendurgan

A moment of quiet on the Helford River

Godolphin

Godolphin Cross, Helston,
Cornwall TR13 9RE

2000 🏠🏛️📷✳️♿

Hidden in shaded woodland, Godolphin escaped modernisation and contemporary fashions. The granite-faced terraces and sunken lawns of the Side Garden have seen little change since the 16th century, and Victorian farm buildings tell the story of Godolphin as a tenant farm. The estate, once busy with prosperous tin mines, is now part of the Cornish Mining World Heritage Site and is wonderful walking country, rich in archaeology, rare plants and wildlife. There are panoramic views from the top of Godolphin Hill. The historic house is a holiday home, where you can stay and experience the splendour that mining riches bought.

The grounds and garden at Godolphin, above and below

Note: house is open to visitors on limited dates between holiday bookings.

Access: 🅿️♿ 🅳♿ 🚾♿ 🏠♿

Find out more: 01736 763194 or godolphin@nationaltrust.org.uk
nationaltrust.org.uk/godolphin

Godrevy

near Hayle, Cornwall 1939

Long sandy beaches on St Ives Bay with wildlife-rich cliffs and walks. **Note**: unstable cliffs and incoming tides. Toilets open in top field. **Satnav**: use TR27 5ED.

Find out more: 01872 552412 or godrevy@nationaltrust.org.uk
nationaltrust.org.uk/godrevy

Gunwalloe

near Helston, Cornwall 1974

Two family-friendly beaches and reedbeds rich in wildlife. Between the two coves a medieval church shelters behind Castle Mound. **Note**: Seasonal beach kiosk. **Satnav**: use TR12 7QE for Gunwalloe car park.

Find out more: 01326 222170 or gunwalloe@nationaltrust.org.uk
nationaltrust.org.uk/gunwalloe

Holywell

near Newquay, Cornwall

1951 🏊 🚾

Classic north Cornish beach, with a sweep of golden sand and a towering dune system. There's lots of history to discover, including the remains of an Iron Age castle on Kelsey Head, a Bronze Age barrow on Cubert Common and the holy well in a cave on the beach. **Satnav**: use TR8 5PF.

Access: 🅿️ 🚾

Holywell's golden sand and enticing sea

Looking out at Carter's Rocks at Holywell

Find out more: 01208 863046 or holywell@nationaltrust.org.uk
nationaltrust.org.uk/holywell

Kynance Cove

on the Lizard peninsula, Cornwall 1935

It's a ⅓-mile walk through Lizard heathland down to this famous beach, with its serpentine stacks, islands and caves. **Note**: steep, uneven beach path. Extremely busy in summer. **Satnav**: use TR12 7PJ.

Find out more: 01326 222170 or kynancecove@nationaltrust.org.uk
nationaltrust.org.uk/kynance-cove

Lanhydrock

Bodmin, Cornwall

1953 🏠 ✝ ✿ ♿

A tragic fire in 1881 meant that the Agar-Robartes family had to rebuild most of their 17th-century home. Out of the ashes came the country house you see today, a fine example of a High Victorian Arts and Crafts interior. Discover the story of the Agar-Robartes in the elegant luxury of the family rooms, and the lives of the staff who lived and worked here.

Lanhydrock, above and below

Outside is a garden, full of colour all year round and famed for its magnolias and ancient woodlands with miles of footpaths to explore. The off-road cycle trails have different routes to suit all levels of experience, and you can even hire a bike when you get here. **Satnav**: use PL30 4AB (1 Double Lodges).

Access: [icons]

Find out more: 01208 265950 or lanhydrock@nationaltrust.org.uk
Bodmin, Cornwall PL30 5AD
nationaltrust.org.uk/lanhydrock

The garden, above, and cycle trails, below, at Lanhydrock

Lansallos

between Polperro and Polruan, Cornwall

1936 [icons]

The unspoilt coastline at Lansallos

East of the Fowey Estuary is a long stretch of unspoilt coast loved by walkers, with abundant wild flowers and birds. From Lansallos church, a path ambles down the valley to a west-facing sandy beach. A picnic and a nose for adventure are all you need for the perfect day. **Note**: nearest toilets at Lantivet Bay car park. **Satnav**: use PL13 2PX for Lansallos.

Find out more: 01726 870146 or lansallos@nationaltrust.org.uk
nationaltrust.org.uk/lansallos

Lantic Bay

near Polruan, Cornwall 1959

Large shingly secluded beach on a beautiful bay, great spot for paddling and picnicking, well worth the climb back up. **Note**: sorry no toilet. Beach is down a very steep path with steps. Beware of rip tides. **Satnav**: use PL23 1NP.

Find out more: 01726 870146 or lanticbay@nationaltrust.org.uk
nationaltrust.org.uk/lantic-bay

Lantivet Bay

between Polruan and Lansallos, Cornwall 1976

Great starting point for walks along this unspoilt sweep of coast, with its small rocky coves. Access to coast path. **Satnav**: use PL23 1NP.

Find out more: 01726 870146 or lantivetbay@nationaltrust.org.uk
nationaltrust.org.uk/lantivet-bay

Lawrence House

9 Castle Street, Launceston, Cornwall PL15 8BA 1964

This Georgian town house, now a museum, hosts special exhibitions. Large display of costumes and a children's toy room. **Note**: leased to Launceston Town Council.

Find out more: 01566 773277 or lawrencehouse@nationaltrust.org.uk
nationaltrust.org.uk/lawrence-house

Levant Mine and Beam Engine

on the Tin Coast, near Pendeen, St Just, Cornwall TR19 7SX

1967

Levant Mine and Beam Engine

High on the cliffs of the Tin Coast is Levant, part of the Cornish Mining World Heritage Site. At its heart is an 1840s beam engine, run on steam. You can discover how Cornish miners, engineers and inventors risked everything in pursuit of mineral riches under the sea. **Note**: exposed clifftop location, uneven ground/mine ruins. Limited space in engine house and small staircases.

Access:

Find out more: 01736 786156 or levant@nationaltrust.org.uk
nationaltrust.org.uk/levant-mine

Underground at Levant Mine

Lizard Point

on the Lizard peninsula, near Helston, Cornwall

1935

This is mainland Britain's most southerly point, infamous as a site of shipwrecks in the past and overlooking what is still one of the busiest shipping lanes in the world. The cliffs and farmland are incredibly rich in wildlife, and in early summer the wild flowers are at their best. From the Wildlife Watchpoint you can spot seals and

Lizard Point, above and below

occasionally dolphins, as well as the iconic Cornish choughs that breed close by. At Bass Point, a short walk along the coast path, you'll find the tiny Lizard Wireless Station. **Satnav**: use TR12 7NT.

Access:

Find out more: 01326 222170 or lizard@nationaltrust.org.uk
nationaltrust.org.uk/lizard-point

Lizard Wireless Station

Bass Point, Lizard, near Helston, Cornwall 1996

The oldest surviving wireless station in the world – a tiny hut on the cliffs where Marconi conducted his world-changing experiments. **Note**: best access by foot from Lizard Point car park, 1 mile along coast path. **Satnav**: use TR12 7NT for Lizard Point car park.

Find out more: 01326 222170 or lizardwirelessstation@nationaltrust.org.uk

Morwenstow

near Bude, Cornwall 1956

Coastal realm of a great Victorian character – Parson Hawker. Hawker's Hut, driftwood-built, is on the cliff edge near his church. **Note**: sorry no toilet. **Satnav**: use EX23 9SR.

Find out more: 01208 863046 or morwenstow@nationaltrust.org.uk
nationaltrust.org.uk/morwenstow

Mullion Cove

on the Lizard peninsula, near Helston, Cornwall 1945

Originally built in the 1890s, the picturesque harbour at Mullion Cove shelters a small fishing fleet from powerful westerly storms. **Note**: toilets open seasonally. National Trust campsite nearby at Teneriffe Farm. **Satnav**: use TR12 7ES.

Find out more: 01326 222170 or mullioncove@nationaltrust.org.uk
nationaltrust.org.uk/mullion-cove

Northcott Mouth

near Bude, Cornwall 1981

Quiet and ruggedly beautiful, this small rocky beach opens up to expansive sand and rock pools as the tide drops. **Note**: sorry no toilet. Lifeguards in high season. **Satnav**: use EX23 9ED.

Find out more: 01208 863046 or northcottmouth@nationaltrust.org.uk
nationaltrust.org.uk/northcott-mouth

Penrose

near Helston and Porthleven, Cornwall

1974 🏛️♿🚗🐾

Home to Loe Pool, Cornwall's largest natural lake, Penrose is a mix of woods, farmland, parkland, cliffs and beaches: a great place to explore. There are 16 miles of bridleways and footpaths, including a trail around the pool and many coast-path links. **Note**: to maintain the sense of peace, fishing and recreational activities aren't allowed on the pool. **Satnav**: use TR13 0RA for Fairground car park and TR13 0RD for Penrose Hill car park.

Find out more: 01326 222170 or penroseestate@nationaltrust.org.uk
nationaltrust.org.uk/penrose

Exploring a wooded path at Penrose

Pentire

near Wadebridge, Cornwall

1936

Carpeted with wild flowers, the farmed headlands of Pentire and The Rumps command views from Tintagel to Trevose Head. Accessible orchard for picnics. **Note**: changing place facilities. **Satnav**: use PL27 6QY for Pentireglaze; PL27 6QZ for Lundy Bay.

Access:

Find out more: 01208 863046 or pentire@nationaltrust.org.uk

Port Quin Bay from The Rumps

Poldhu Cove

near Mullion, Cornwall

1984

Unspoilt Poldhu Cove

This unspoilt beach is popular with locals and visitors. The beach, dunes and reedbeds are designated as a Site of Special Scientific Interest for their rich wildlife. South of the cove the Marconi Monument and visitor centre celebrate Poldhu's role as the site of the first transatlantic wireless signal. **Note:** beach is life guarded through peak season. **Satnav**: use TR12 7BU.

Access:

Find out more: 01326 222170 or poldhucove@nationaltrust.org.uk
nationaltrust.org.uk/poldhu-cove

Port Quin

near Wadebridge, Cornwall 1936

Sheltered inlet on outstanding stretch of unspoilt coast. **Satnav**: use PL29 3SU.

Find out more: 01208 863046 or portquin@nationaltrust.org.uk
nationaltrust.org.uk/port-quin

Porth

on the Roseland peninsula,
near Portscatho, Cornwall 1958

The creekside and coastal footpaths are
great for walking and wildlife-spotting, or
spend the day on the beach at Towan.
Satnav: use TR2 5EX.

Find out more: 01872 501062 or
porth@nationaltrust.org.uk
nationaltrust.org.uk/porth

Porthcurno

near Penzance, Cornwall 1994

Popular sandy beach on a turquoise bay.
Great for watching birds and spotting
marine wildlife from the cliffs above.
Satnav: use TR19 6JU.

Find out more: 01736 761853 or
porthcurno@nationaltrust.org.uk
nationaltrust.org.uk/porthcurno

St Agnes Head

near St Agnes, Cornwall 1967

A patchwork of gorse and heather carpets
these clifftops high above the Atlantic
Ocean, overlooked by lofty St Agnes
Beacon. **Satnav**: use TR5 0NU.

Find out more: 01872 552412 or
stagneshead@nationaltrust.org.uk
nationaltrust.org.uk/st-agnes-head

*Looking out from the Battery Observation
Post on St Anthony Head, top right, and the
view towards St Mawes, right*

St Anthony Head

on the Roseland peninsula,
near Portscatho, Cornwall

1959

Standing guard on the eastern entrance to
Falmouth Harbour, this headland has been
strategically important for centuries. It
commands magnificent views up the Fal
Estuary and across Falmouth Bay towards
the Lizard, and you'll find plenty of historic
fortifications from various eras to explore.
Satnav: use TR2 5HA.

Access: ♿

Find out more: 01872 501062 or
stanthonyhead@nationaltrust.org.uk
nationaltrust.org.uk/st-anthony-head

St Michael's Mount: looking up at the medieval castle and church

Check opening dates and times before you set out: nationaltrust.org.uk

St Michael's Mount

Marazion, Cornwall TR17 0HS

1954 ☒ ✝ ✿ ⌖

Iconic St Michael's Mount, as seen from Marazion

This iconic rocky island, crowned by a medieval church and castle, is home to the St Aubyn family and a 30-strong community of islanders. Visiting the Mount, you are immersed in history, islanders' tales and legends, such as the famous 'Jack the Giant Killer'. There's a subtropical terraced garden to explore, and spectacular views of Mount's Bay and the Lizard from the castle battlements. If the tide is high, you can take an evocative boat trip to the island harbour; at low tide you walk across the ancient cobbled causeway from Marazion on the mainland, as pilgrims have done for centuries. **Note**: steep climb to the castle over uneven, cobbled, historic pathway. St Aubyn Estates/National Trust partnership. Members have to pay for car parking and boat trips to the Mount.

Access: P♿ ♿WC ⌘

Find out more: 01736 710265 (information, tides and boats) or stmichaelsmount@nationaltrust.org.uk Estate Office, King's Road, Marazion TR17 0EL **nationaltrust.org.uk/st-michaels-mount stmichaelsmount.co.uk**

Sandymouth

near Bude, Cornwall

1978 ⌖

A popular destination, yet Sandymouth remains unspoilt and breathtakingly beautiful. You'll find an extreme difference between the beach at low tide – when it is a huge sweep of sand and rocky outcrops – and at high tide, when it shrinks back to a pebbly cove, backed by twisted cliffs. **Satnav**: use EX23 9HW.

Access: P♿ ♿WC

Find out more: 01208 863046 or sandymouth@nationaltrust.org.uk **nationaltrust.org.uk/sandymouth**

Sandymouth at low tide

Surfing at Sandymouth

Tintagel Old Post Office

Fore Street, Tintagel, Cornwall PL34 0DB

1903 🏠 ❖

The fireplace at Tintagel Old Post Office

A medieval manor house in miniature, at more than 600 years old this is one of Cornwall's oldest domestic buildings. Used by a number of businesses throughout the Victorian period, its final function was as the village's letter-receiving office. The cottage garden hidden at the back offers a welcome retreat.

Access: 🚶

Find out more: 01840 770024 or tintageloldpo@nationaltrust.org.uk
nationaltrust.org.uk/tintagel-old-post-office

Trelissick

Feock, near Truro, Cornwall TR3 6QL

1955 🏠 🏛 ❖ 🍴 🏛

Set on its own peninsula, Trelissick enjoys panoramic views over the Fal Estuary, and the south terrace provides the perfect setting to enjoy the ever-changing seascape and countryside. Visitors can explore meandering paths through the garden, leading to exotic planting and formal lawns with herbaceous borders bursting with colour. There are also longer walks to discover through the historic park and woodland, which sweep down towards the estuary, and along Lamouth Creek to the Iron Age promontory fort and 18th-century quay at Roundwood.

Trelissick house and parkland, above and below

Access: 🅿️ 🚻 ♿ 🚲 ♿

Find out more: 01872 862090 or
trelissick@nationaltrust.org.uk
nationaltrust.org.uk/trelissick

Trengwainton Garden

Madron, near Penzance,
Cornwall TR20 8RZ

1961 ❖

Here in this sheltered garden you can follow
in the footsteps of the 1920s plant hunters
to see colourful species that were the first
of their kind to flower in Britain. Award-
winning magnolias and rhododendrons are
still nurtured by those with a passion for
plants, and subtropical varieties from
around the world thrive in the shelter of the
walled gardens, which contain a kitchen
garden built to the dimensions of Noah's
Ark. Winding wooded paths follow a

**The stream and meadow at
Trengwainton Garden**

The productive kitchen garden, above, and sea views, below, at Trengwainton

half-mile incline offering sea views across Mount's Bay, and the descent via the drive is bordered by a stream garden and open meadows.

Access: 🅿️🅳♿✍️♿👁️

Find out more: 01736 363148 or trengwainton@nationaltrust.org.uk
nationaltrust.org.uk/trengwainton

Trerice

near Newquay, Cornwall

1953 🏠❄️

Once the Cornish seat of the Arundell family, Trerice remains little changed since it was built in 1573, thanks to long periods under absentee owners. With golden stone, ornate gables and a magnificent hall window, Trerice is a grand Elizabethan house on a small scale. From the highest

Trerice, left and above, is a grand
Elizabethan house on a small scale

point of the garden, views stretch out over
a landscape rich in history. Shouts of
excitement ring out from the kayling lawn
as the Cornish game of 'kayles' is played,
bringing back some of the bustle and noise
that must have typified Trerice's time as a
working manor farm. **Note**: we occasionally
need to close parts or all of Trerice for
private functions. **Satnav**: enter Kestle Mill
via A3058, not postcode.

Access: 🅿️ 🅿️ 🚻 ♿ ♿

Find out more: 01637 875404 or
trerice@nationaltrust.org.uk
Kestle Mill, near Newquay, Cornwall TR8 4PG
nationaltrust.org.uk/trerice

Trevose Head

near Padstow, Cornwall

2016 🔭

View from Trevose Head

Jutting into the Atlantic, Trevose Head
commands views for miles along the coast.
Exposed western cliffs contrast starkly with
a gentler eastern coastline. Home of
Trevose Lighthouse (owned by Trinity
House) and Padstow Lifeboat Station, it's
also famed for nesting corn buntings and
skylarks, and rare plants like wild asparagus.
Note: sorry no toilet. Be careful of the
sheer-sided round hole and quarry near
Dinas Head. **Satnav**: use PL28 8SL.

Find out more: 01208 863046 or
trevosehead@nationaltrust.org.uk
nationaltrust.org.uk/trevose

Wheal Coates

near St Agnes, Cornwall 1956

Dramatic mining ruins – an iconic Cornish
sight – hugging the heather and gorse-
carpeted clifftops. **Satnav**: use TR5 0NT.

Find out more: 01872 552412 or
whealcoates@nationaltrust.org.uk
nationaltrust.org.uk/wheal-coates

Devon and Dorset

A riot of summer flowers
at Hardy's Cottage in Dorset

Lundy

Mortehoe
Woolacombe
Baggy Point
Ilfracombe
Bude

Heddon
Valley

Arlington Court

Lorna Doone
Valley

Watersmeet

Barnstaple

Bideford

Coteheie

Lydford
Gorge

Buckland
Abbey

Launceston

Okehampton

Dunster
Castle

Knightshayes

TAUNTON

Finch Foundry

South Milton Sands
Bolberry Down

Wembury
Saltram
PLYMOUTH

Cadover Bridge
Plymbridge Woods
Shaugh Bridge

Castle
Drogo

Fingle Bridge

Clyston Mill
Killerton

Budlake Old
Post Office

Ashclyst
Forest

Tiverton

Barrington Court

Lytes Cary
Manor

East Soar
Overbeck's
Garden

Mill Bay
Salcombe

Dartmouth

Greenway

Compton
Castle

Bradley

Parke

EXETER

Marker's

A la Ronde

Honiton

Loughwood
Meeting House

Montacute
House

Mompesson
House

Little Dartmouth
Brownstone
Coleton Fishacre
Coleton Camp

Paignton

Newton Abbot

Torquay

Exmouth

Sidmouth

Branscombe

Bridport

Golden
Cap

Burton
Bradstock

Yeovil

Stourhead

Salisbury

Weymouth

DORCHESTER

Hardy
Monument

Max Gate
Hardy's
Cottage

Kingston Lacy
White Mill

Poole
BOURNEMOUTH

Ringstead
Bay

Clouds Hill
Corfe
Castle

Brownsea Island
Studland Bay

Spyway

To discover more coastal and countryside
car parks in Devon and Dorset, go to
nationaltrust.org.uk/carparks

Places in neighbouring counties

Buildings and/or gardens

Entry points to
coast and countryside

National Trust land

Cornwall, page 20

Somerset and Wiltshire, page 82

10 miles

A la Ronde

Exmouth, Devon

1991

Full of creativity and treasures from around the world, this amazing 16-sided house was the work of cousins Jane and Mary Parminter in the 1790s. Step inside and enter another world, one where their imaginations ran wild in design and ornamentation. They decorated walls with feathers, shells and pictures made of seaweed and sand, and every space contains mementoes from their travels. With the 360° touchscreen virtual tour, you can view the fragile shell gallery made with 25,000 shells. Outside, there's a sense of harmony around the orchard, hay meadow and colourful borders, and views over the Exe Estuary. **Note**: small and delicate rooms. Photography welcome without flash.

A la Ronde, Devon: eccentric and captivating inside and out

Satnav: postcode unreliable, enter Summer Lane.

Access:

Find out more: 01395 265514 or alaronde@nationaltrust.org.uk Summer Lane, Exmouth, Devon EX8 5BD **nationaltrust.org.uk/a-la-ronde**

Access: 🅿♿♿♿♿

Arlington Court and the National Trust Carriage Museum

Find out more: 01271 850296 or
arlingtoncourt@nationaltrust.org.uk
nationaltrust.org.uk/arlington

Exploring Arlington Court and the National Trust Carriage Museum in Devon, above and below

Arlington, near Barnstaple, Devon EX31 4LP

1949 ♞✝♿♣♘

Hidden in the lichen-draped landscape of North Devon, Arlington is a surprise and a delight. The starkly classical exterior of the house gives no clue to what lies inside – recently redisplayed to share the passions of the Chichester family who lived here. The stable block houses a nationally important display of more than 40 carriages, from grand state coaches to humble governess cars. The garden is restored to its colourful Victorian glory, and the conservatory's exotic plantings reveal the Chichesters' world travels. **Satnav:** from South Molton, don't turn left into unmarked lane (deliveries only).

Baggy Point

near Croyde, Devon

1939

Baggy Point is the impressive headland at Croyde, once owned by the Hyde family and overlooking one of the best surfing beaches in the South West. Huge coastal views out to Lundy Island, great walking and opportunities to climb, surf and coasteer make it a must-do destination for anyone visiting North Devon. Baggy Point also appeals to wildlife and nature lovers – keep a look out for seals and porpoises, as well as many bird species, including peregrine falcons, linnets and Dartford warblers. **Note**: toilets and outdoor shower in courtyard next to car park. **Satnav**: use EX33 1PA.

Baggy Point, Devon: the impressive headland, above and below, offers coastal walks

Access:

Find out more: 01271 870555 or baggypoint@nationaltrust.org.uk **nationaltrust.org.uk/baggy-point**

Bolberry Down

between Salcombe and Hope Cove,
near Malborough, Devon

 1938 ☕🚶

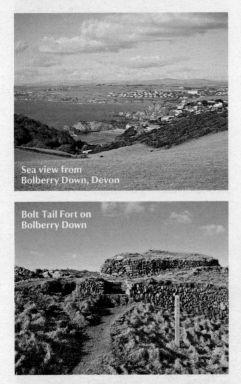

Sea view from
Bolberry Down, Devon

Bolt Tail Fort on
Bolberry Down

The starting point for a spectacular stretch
of coast between Salcombe and Hope
Cove, including the headlands of Bolt Head
and Bolt Tail and the sandy beach at Soar
Mill Cove. The majestic rugged cliffs have
claimed countless ships over the centuries.
There's an easy-access clifftop route.
Satnav: use TQ7 3DY.

Access: P🅿 🚶

Find out more: 01752 346585 or
bolberrydown@nationaltrust.org.uk
nationaltrust.org.uk/bolberry-down

Bradley

Newton Abbot, Devon

1938 🏠✝🌸

Surrounded by riverside meadows and
woodland, this unspoilt medieval manor
house is still a relaxed family home. There
are original features to look out for, such as
the medieval cat hole and drip stones,
as well as the peaceful chapel that was
licensed for services in 1428.
Note: sorry no toilet.
Satnav: TQ12 1LX directs to gate lodge.

Access: P🅿 🅿🅳 🚶

Find out more: 01803 661907 or
bradley@nationaltrust.org.uk
Totnes Road, Newton Abbot,
Devon TQ12 6BN
nationaltrust.org.uk/bradley

Bradley in Devon is relaxed and unspoilt

Branscombe

on the Jurassic Coast, near Seaton, Devon

1965 🏛️♿🛏️

Nestling in a valley that reaches down to the sea on East Devon's dramatic Jurassic Coast, the village of Branscombe is surrounded by picturesque countryside with miles of tranquil walking through woodland, farmland and beach. Charming

Branscombe, Devon: nestled in a valley by the sea

thatched houses, forge and restored watermill add to the timeless magic of the place. **Note**: nearest toilets (not National Trust) at information point, village hall and beach car park. **Satnav**: use EX12 3DB.

Access: ♿

Find out more: 01752 346585 or branscombe@nationaltrust.org.uk
nationaltrust.org.uk/branscombe

Brownsea Island

Poole Harbour, Poole, Dorset

1962 ✝️🏛️♿🛏️🐾

The perfect day's adventure, this island wildlife sanctuary is easy to get to but feels like a million miles away as soon as you step ashore. Wander through sheltered woodland, sweeping shorelines and dramatic clifftops, spotting wildlife as you go, such as the rare red squirrel. The internationally important lagoon also plays host to thousands of birds that fly in from distant lands throughout the season. As the

Brownsea Island, Dorset, offers adventures galore

An easily accessible route at Brownsea Island

birthplace of Scouting and Guiding, the island is the perfect place for your very own outdoor adventure, with free family trails and natural play area. **Note:** see website for ferry information. *Seahorse* wheelchair ferry service available. Voluntary donation to enter the Dorset Wildlife Trust area (including members). No visitor or member access to castle. **Satnav:** for Sandbanks Jetty use BH13 7QJ; for Poole Quay BH15 1HP.

Access: 🈺 ♿ ♿

Find out more: 01202 707744 or brownseaisland@nationaltrust.org.uk **nationaltrust.org.uk/brownsea-island**

Brownstone

Brownstone Road, Kingswear, Devon TQ6 0EH 1981

Spectacular views on a coastal walk that leads to a rare Second World War gun battery at Froward Point. **Note:** naturally uneven coastal paths, steep in places – be aware of cliff edges.

Find out more: 01803 752776 (rangers) or brownstone@nationaltrust.org.uk **nationaltrust.org.uk/brownstone**

Buckland Abbey

Yelverton, Devon

1948 🏛 ✝ ❁ 🐾

Hundreds of years ago, Cistercian monks chose this tranquil valley as the perfect spot in which to worship, farm their estate and trade. The Abbey, later converted into a house, today combines furnished rooms with museum galleries, bringing to life the story of how seafaring adventurers Sir Richard Grenville and Sir Francis Drake changed the shape of Buckland Abbey and the fate of England. Outdoors you'll find the formal Elizabethan garden, walled kitchen garden and Cider House garden; the impressive medieval Great Barn; orchards and woodland walks with far-reaching views and late spring bluebells.

Satnav: follow brown signs, not satnav.

Access: [icons]

Find out more: 01822 853607 or
bucklandabbey@nationaltrust.org.uk
Yelverton, Devon PL20 6EY
nationaltrust.org.uk/buckland-abbey

There are so many stories to discover at tranquil Buckland Abbey in Devon, above and below

Burton Bradstock

on the Jurassic Coast, near Bridport, Dorset

1973

One of the main gateways to Dorset's Jurassic Coast. Here are spectacular sandstone cliffs – Burton Cliff glows bright gold in sunlight – and miles of unspoilt beaches. Hive Beach is a popular family destination, nearby Cogden is quieter; both are part of Chesil Bank, the largest shingle ridge in the world. **Satnav**: use DT6 4RF for Burton Bradstock; DT6 4RL for Cogden.

Popular Burton Bradstock in Dorset

Access: [icon]

Find out more: 01297 489481 or
burtonbradstock@nationaltrust.org.uk
nationaltrust.org.uk/burton-bradstock

Cadover Bridge

on Dartmoor, near Shaugh Prior, Devon
1960

Tranquil moorland by River Plym, with pools. Starting point for walks through ancient woodland or across open moors and tors. **Satnav**: use PL7 5EH.

Find out more:
cadoverbridge@nationaltrust.org.uk
nationaltrust.org.uk/cadover-bridge

Castle Drogo

Drewsteignton, near Exeter,
Devon EX6 6PB

1974 🏠🖼️✝️❀♨️

High above the ancient woodlands of the Teign Gorge on the edge of Dartmoor stands Castle Drogo. Reminiscent of a medieval fortress, the castle was designed and built between 1910 and 1930 by the renowned architect Sir Edwin Lutyens for the self-made millionaire Julius Drewe. Inside the imposing granite walls, the ingenuity of Lutyens's design is revealed in grand show rooms, functional servants' spaces and comfortable family rooms, perfectly suited to the lifestyle of a modern 20th-century family. Outside, hidden behind immaculate yew hedges, the garden is a perfect partnership of colourful seasonal planting with Lutyens's formal architectural design.

Access: ♿🅿️♿🚻🔊♿♿

Find out more: 01647 433306 or castledrogo@nationaltrust.org.uk
nationaltrust.org.uk/castle-drogo

Castle Drogo in Devon, above and below

Clouds Hill

Bovington, Dorset BH20 7NQ

1937

Clouds Hill in Dorset: T. E. Lawrence's home

In this tiny woodsman's cottage you can discover the essentials and the luxuries chosen by T. E. Lawrence after he had abandoned the 'Lawrence of Arabia' persona and remodelled himself as a private in the army at Bovington Camp. Much of the furniture and fittings was designed by Lawrence himself.

Find out more: 01929 405616 or cloudshill@nationaltrust.org.uk
nationaltrust.org.uk/clouds-hill

Coleton Camp

between Dart Estuary and Brixham, Devon 1981

Great walks along the coast path to Scabbacombe and Man Sands beaches on this rugged stretch of coast. **Note**: naturally uneven coastal paths, steep in places – be aware of cliff edges. **Satnav**: use TQ6 0EQ.

Find out more: 01803 753010 or coletoncamp@nationaltrust.org.uk
nationaltrust.org.uk/brownstone-and-coleton-camp

Coleton Fishacre

Brownstone Road, Kingswear, Devon TQ6 0EQ

1982

This evocative 1920s Arts and Crafts-style house, with its elegant art deco interiors, perfectly encapsulates the spirit of the Jazz Age. The former country home of the D'Oyly Carte family, it has a light, joyful atmosphere with touches of a bygone era.

Coleton Fishacre in Devon: the house and garden, below and bottom

The RHS-accredited garden at Coleton Fishacre, above and top

You can glimpse life 'downstairs' in the servants' rooms. In the RHS-accredited garden, paths weave through glades and past tranquil ponds and rare tender plants from New Zealand and South Africa; many exotic plants thrive beneath the tree canopy. You can walk down through the valley garden to a coastal viewpoint with inspiring sea views.

Access: 🅿♿♿♿♿♿

Find out more: 01803 842382 or coletonfishacre@nationaltrust.org.uk
nationaltrust.org.uk/coleton-fishacre

Compton Castle

Marldon, Paignton, Devon TQ3 1TA

1951 🏰✝❀♿

A rare survivor, this medieval fortified manor house has high curtain walls and portcullises. It was once the home of Sir Humphrey Gilbert, part-founder of the New World, and his descendants still live here today. Outside, you can discover roses climbing pergolas, knot and herb gardens and a picnic orchard. **Note**: hall, sub-solar, solar, study, kitchen, scullery, guard room, chapel open.

Access: ♿♿

Find out more: 01803 661906 or comptoncastle@nationaltrust.org.uk
nationaltrust.org.uk/compton-castle

Medieval Compton Castle in Devon

Corfe Castle

near Wareham, Dorset

1982

This fairy-tale fortress is an evocative survivor of the English Civil War, partially demolished by the Parliamentarians in 1646. It's a favourite haunt for adults and children alike – all ages are captivated by these romantic ruins with their breathtaking views. There are 1,000 years

Corfe Castle, Dorset, above and below

Corfe Castle's brooding presence, above and right, reflects its tragic history of treachery and treason

of the castle's history as a royal palace and fortress to be discovered here. Fallen walls and secret places tell tales of treachery and treason around every corner. Corfe Castle's brooding presence is a backdrop to some of Britain's most beautiful coast and countryside. Corfe Common and Hartland Moor are close by – you can explore them by walking or cycling, discovering rare wild flowers and masses of wildlife along the way. **Note**: steep, uneven slopes; steps; sudden drops throughout castle. All/parts of castle close in high winds. **Satnav**: use BH20 5DR.

Access: 🅿️ ♿ ♿ ♫

Find out more: 01929 477063 (ticket office) or corfecastle@nationaltrust.org.uk Corfe, near Wareham, Dorset BH20 5EZ **nationaltrust.org.uk/corfe-castle**

East Soar

between Salcombe and Hope Cove,
near Malborough, Devon

1950

**Soar Mill Cove, near East Soar
in Devon**

This is a great starting point for exploring
the isolated and rugged coast between
Bolt Head and Bolt Tail. There's so much
history to discover, including the remains
of Bronze Age settlements, shipwrecks and
'orthostats' (ancient field boundary stones).
There is a waymarked 1-mile route to
Overbeck's, overlooking Salcombe.
Satnav: use TQ7 3DR.

Access: P&

Find out more: 01752 346585.
01548 561904 (East Soar Outdoor
Experience) or
eastsoar@nationaltrust.org.uk
nationaltrust.org.uk/east-soar

Finch Foundry

Sticklepath, Okehampton,
Devon EX20 2NW

1994

Working the forge at Finch Foundry, Devon

The foundry was a 19th-century family-run
business producing a range of tools for
West Country industries, including farming
and mining. Products of the business are
displayed in the carpenters' workshop.
Outside is a delightful cottage garden.
Note: narrow entrance to car park,
plus height restrictions.

Access: D&

Find out more: 01647 433306 or
finchfoundry@nationaltrust.org.uk
nationaltrust.org.uk/finch-foundry

Fingle Bridge

near Drewsteignton, Devon 1990

Popular spot in Dartmoor's Teign Gorge.
Walkers can explore the footpaths in
nearby Fingle Woods, or climb towards
Castle Drogo. **Note**: uneven terrain. Fingle
Woods are being restored and managed in
partnership with the Woodland Trust.
Satnav: use EX6 6PW.

Find out more:
finglebridge@nationaltrust.org.uk
nationaltrust.org.uk/fingle-bridge

Golden Cap

on the Jurassic Coast, near Bridport, Dorset

| 1961 | 🏖️ |

Golden Cap in Dorset is the highest point on the south coast

Spectacular countryside estate on the Jurassic Coast – one of England's natural World Heritage Sites. The great rocky shoulder of Golden Cap is the south coast's highest point, with breathtaking views in all directions. Stonebarrow Hill is a good starting point for discovering the 25 miles of footpaths around the estate.
Satnav: for Stonebarrow use DT6 6RA; Langdon Hill DT6 6EP.

Access: 👓

Find out more: 01297 489481 or goldencap@nationaltrust.org.uk
nationaltrust.org.uk/golden-cap

Greenway

Greenway Road, Galmpton, near Brixham, Devon TQ5 0ES

| 2000 | 🏛️ |

Here you are given a glimpse into the lives of the famous author Agatha Christie and her family. Their holiday home is set in the 1950s, when Greenway overflowed with friends and family gathered together for holidays and Christmas. The family were great collectors: the house is brimming with their books, archaeology, Tunbridgeware, silver and porcelain. The informal woodland garden drifts down the hillside towards the Dart Estuary and the Boathouse, scene of the crime in *Dead Man's Folly*. Please consider 'green ways' to travel here: ferry (courtesy vehicle available from quay), cycling or walking. **Note**: booking essential for parking.

Access: 🅿️

Agatha Christie and her family loved their holidays at Greenway in Devon. Set in the 1950s, the house is full of their collections

Find out more: 01803 842382 (car-park booking and infoline). 01803 882811 (ferry). or greenway@nationaltrust.org.uk
nationaltrust.org.uk/greenway

Hardy Monument

Black Down, near Portesham, Dorset 1938

Memorial to Vice-Admiral Hardy, Flag-Captain of HMS *Victory* at Trafalgar, designed to look like a spyglass. Views over the Channel.
Satnav: nearest postcode is DT2 9HY.

Find out more: 01305 262538. 01297 489481 or hardymonument@nationaltrust.org.uk
nationaltrust.org.uk/hardy-monument

Hardy's Cottage

Higher Bockhampton, near Dorchester, Dorset DT2 8QJ

1948

Hardy's Cottage in Dorset, the birthplace of Thomas Hardy, above and top

You can find yourself 'far from the madding crowd', as you discover Hardy's rural childhood home, with its quintessential cottage garden, and the birthplace of his literary land of 'Wessex'. **Note**: nearest toilet at visitor centre.

Access:

Find out more: 01305 262366 or hardyscottage@nationaltrust.org.uk
nationaltrust.org.uk/hardys-cottage

Heddon Valley in Devon, above and below, lies on the dramatic West Exmoor coast

Heddon Valley

on Exmoor, near Combe Martin, Devon

1963 🏛️🛏️♿⚓

The dramatic West Exmoor coast, favourite landscape of the Romantic poets, offers not only the beautiful Heddon Valley to explore, but also Woody Bay and the Hangman Hills nearby. At the heart of the valley sits the historic Hunter's Inn, a good place to relax after discovering the spectacular coastal, moorland and woodland walks in the area. Nature highlights include one of the UK's last surviving colonies of high brown fritillary butterflies, which can be seen in June and July on the bracken-clad hillsides of Heddon Valley. Look out for the rich diversity of fungi in autumn. **Satnav**: use EX31 4PY.

Access: 🅿️♿🔍📷♿

Find out more: 01598 763402 or heddonvalley@nationaltrust.org.uk
nationaltrust.org.uk/heddon-valley

Killerton

Broadclyst, Exeter, Devon EX5 3LE

1944 🏠✝🏛♣🎖

Would you give away your family home for your political beliefs? Sir Richard Acland did just that with his Killerton Estate in the heart of Devon, when he gave it to the Trust in 1944. Today you'll find a welcoming Georgian house set in 2,600 hectares (6,400 acres) of working farmland, woods, parkland, cottages and orchards. There's plenty of

Learning about Killerton

Killerton in Devon: the warm and welcoming Georgian house

Killerton's glorious grounds offer winding paths, an Iron Age hill fort and even an extinct volcano

calm space in the glorious garden, beautiful year-round with rhododendrons, magnolias, champion trees and formal lawns. You can explore winding paths, climb an extinct volcano, discover an Iron Age hill fort and take in distant views towards Dartmoor. More family home than grand mansion, the relaxed house holds the National Trust's largest fashion collection, with selected items exhibited annually. **Satnav**: on arrival, follow brown signs to main car park.

Access: ⬛⬛⬛⬛⬛⬛

Find out more: 01392 881345 or killerton@nationaltrust.org.uk
nationaltrust.org.uk/killerton

Killerton Estate: Ashclyst Forest

near Broadclyst, Exeter, Devon 1944

One of the largest woods in East Devon. A haven for butterflies, bluebells and birds.
Satnav: use EX5 3DT.

Find out more: 01392 881345 or ashclystforest@nationaltrust.org.uk
nationaltrust.org.uk/ashclyst-forest

Killerton Estate: Budlake Old Post Office

Broadclyst, Exeter, Devon EX5 3LW 1944

Visiting is like stepping back into the 1950s.
Note: nearest toilets at Killerton.

Find out more: 01392 881345 or
budlakepostoffice@nationaltrust.org.uk
nationaltrust.org.uk/budlake-old-post-office

Killerton Estate: Clyston Mill

Broadclyst, Exeter, Devon EX5 3EW 1944

A historic working water-powered corn mill
in a picturesque setting by the River Clyst.
Note: nearest toilets in Broadclyst village.

Find out more: 01392 462425 or
clystonmill@nationaltrust.org.uk
nationaltrust.org.uk/clyston-mill

Killerton Estate: Marker's

Broadclyst, Exeter, Devon EX5 3HS 1944

Medieval hall-house with a rare painted
screen, garden and cob summerhouse.
Note: nearest toilets in Broadclyst village.

Find out more: 01392 461546 or
markers@nationaltrust.org.uk
nationaltrust.org.uk/markers

Kingston Lacy

Wimborne Minster, Dorset

1982 ♿ 🏛 🌸 🍴

Home to the Bankes family for over
300 years, Kingston Lacy is a monument
to the family's exceptional taste and desire
to surround themselves with beauty.

**Kingston Lacy, Dorset: accessible path,
below, and the exceptional house, bottom**

After the family lost their Corfe Castle stronghold to the Parliamentarians in the Civil War, they moved here and gradually created an astonishing Italian palace in the heart of rural Dorset. Today you can discover an internationally acclaimed art collection, including paintings by Rubens, Velázquez and Titian, exquisite carvings and lavish interiors. There's even more to explore outside, with sweeping lawns, a Japanese Garden, kitchen garden, woodland and parkland walks – look out for the award-winning herd of Red Ruby Devon cattle – and a huge 3,500-hectare (8,500-acre) countryside estate to enjoy.

Kingston Lacy has the most astonishing collection of Old Masters, as well as lavish interiors and exquisite carvings

Note: some rooms may close at short notice. Low light levels. **Satnav**: unreliable, follow B3082 to main entrance. Use BH21 4EL for Eye Bridge; BH21 4EE for Pamphill Green; DT11 9JL for Badbury Rings.

Access: 🅿️♿🚾✍️♿♿

Find out more: 01202 883402 or kingstonlacy@nationaltrust.org.uk Wimborne Minster, Dorset BH21 4EA **nationaltrust.org.uk/kingston-lacy**

Knightshayes

near Tiverton, Devon

1972

With one of the finest gardens in the South West, Knightshayes is a masterpiece of architectural planting, home to one of the most outstanding botanical collections in the country. Among champion trees, including first introductions to this country, there are hidden glades and pathways to discover far-reaching views. The Gothic Revival house is a rare example of the genius of William Burges, whose opulent designs have inspired extremes of opinion, even among the family who commissioned them. The walled garden combines full

Knightshayes in Devon, above and below

Victorian stained glass at Knightshayes

productivity with aesthetic appeal and is an excellent example of a restored Victorian kitchen garden. **Note**: access to the house and garden is restricted during spring and winter. **Satnav**: do not use, follow brown signs on nearing Tiverton/Bolham.

Access: 🅿️♿️🅿️♿️⬇️♿️

Find out more: 01884 254665 or knightshayes@nationaltrust.org.uk Bolham, near Tiverton, Devon EX16 7RQ **nationaltrust.org.uk/knightshayes**

Lorna Doone Valley

near Lynton, Devon

2020 🖼️

Lorna Doone Valley in Devon

Made famous by R. D. Blackmore in his novel *Lorna Doone*, this mystical valley is a gateway to many inspiring walks. You can extend your time here by staying at Cloud Farm Campsite. **Satnav**: use EX35 6NU.

Access: 🚻

Find out more: 01271 891970 or lornadoonevalley@nationaltrust.org.uk **nationaltrust.org.uk/lorna-doone-valley**

Little Dartmouth

near Dartmouth, Devon 1970

A gentle coastal landscape west of Dartmouth, with wonderful views, wild flowers and the remains of a Civil War encampment. **Note**: Compass Cottage holiday let – ideal base for exploring Dartmouth and the coast. **Satnav**: use TQ6 0JP.

Find out more: 01752 346585 or littledartmouth@nationaltrust.org.uk **nationaltrust.org.uk/little-dartmouth**

Loughwood Meeting House

Dalwood, Axminster, Devon EX13 7DU 1969

Atmospheric 17th-century thatched Baptist meeting house dug into the hillside. **Note**: sorry no toilet.

Find out more: 01752 346585 or loughwood@nationaltrust.org.uk **nationaltrust.org.uk/loughwood-meeting-house**

Lundy

Bristol Channel, Devon

1969

Lundy is a remarkable island in the Bristol Channel, a place of solitude, stark beauty and abundant wildlife, much loved by its regular visitors and residents. A day trip on the MS *Oldenburg* allows time to explore the rugged clifftops, discover seabirds and visit the church, castle and welcoming tavern. **Note**: Lundy is owned by the National Trust, and run by the Landmark Trust. The *Oldenburg* runs from Bideford or Ilfracombe, charge including members (discounts available). **Satnav**: use EX34 9EQ for Ilfracombe; EX39 2EY for Bideford.

Access:

Find out more: 01271 863636 or lundy@nationaltrust.org.uk
The Lundy Shore Office, The Quay, Bideford, Devon EX39 2LY
nationaltrust.org.uk/lundy
lundyisland.co.uk

Lundy, Devon: island of solitude and stark beauty

Lydford Gorge

Lydford, near Tavistock, Devon

1947

Lydford Gorge in Devon

This steep-sided river gorge carved into the western edge of Dartmoor has been drawing visitors in search of the picturesque since Victorian times. It is a truly breathtaking experience. Around every corner the River Lyd plunges, tumbles, swirls and gently meanders as it travels through the steep-sided, oak-wooded valley, which is abundant with wildlife. Walking through the gorge (the deepest in the South West) is a challenging but rewarding adventure. There is a range of trails to suit different abilities and timescales.

Max Gate

Dorchester, Dorset

1940 🏠 ❖

Max Gate, home to Dorset's most famous author and poet, Thomas Hardy, was designed by the writer himself in 1885. This atmospheric Victorian house is where Hardy wrote some of his most famous novels, including *Tess of the d'Urbervilles* and *Jude the Obscure*, as well as most of his poetry. **Satnav**: enter Max Gate, not the postcode.

Access: 🦽

Visitors of all ages enjoy atmospheric Max Gate in Dorset, below, bottom and top right

The steep-sided, oak-wooded valley of Lydford Gorge, above and top

Note: sturdy footwear – rugged terrain, vertical drops. Booking required for Tramper. **Satnav**: EX20 4BH (Devil's Cauldron entrance); EX20 4BL (waterfall entrance).

Access: 🅿️ 🚼 🦽 ♿

Find out more: 01647 433306 or lydfordgorge@nationaltrust.org.uk
nationaltrust.org.uk/lydford-gorge

Find out more: 01305 262538 or
maxgate@nationaltrust.org.uk   Alington
Avenue, Dorchester, Dorset DT1 2FN
nationaltrust.org.uk/max-gate

Mill Bay

East Portlemouth,
near Salcombe, Devon 1991

There are sandy beaches at Mill Bay, Sunny
Cove and Seacombe Sands, with rugged
walking past coastguard lookouts towards
Prawle. **Satnav**: use TQ8 8PU.

Find out more: 01752 346585 or
millbay@nationaltrust.org.uk
nationaltrust.org.uk/mill-bay

Mortehoe

near Ilfracombe, Devon 1909

Gateway to a wild, remote coast with a
rich history of wrecking and smuggling.
Amazing walking, wildlife and sunbathing
seals. **Note**: use EX34 7DT for village car
park and toilets, not National Trust (charge
including members). Town Farmhouse
(tenant-run) offers cream teas in summer.
Satnav: use EX34 7DT.

Find out more: 01271 870555 or
mortehoe@nationaltrust.org.uk
nationaltrust.org.uk/mortehoe

Overbeck's Garden

Sharpitor, Salcombe, Devon TQ8 8LW

1937

Carved into the cliff-side high above
the sea, Overbeck's Garden overlooks
the Salcombe Estuary. Its extraordinary
position not only provides breathtaking
views but also allows tender plants to
flourish, a factor that previous owners
were well aware of as they quite literally
sowed the seeds of the exotic and
subtropical. This terraced garden,
laid out in 1985, hosts a collection of
unusual plants from across the world.

Overbeck's Garden in Devon
is carved into a cliff-side
high above the estuary

Note: entrance path and grounds are very steep in places. **Satnav**: follow brown signs through Salcombe. Large vehicles use TQ7 3DR (1½ miles).

Access: [icons]

Find out more: 01548 842893 or overbecks@nationaltrust.org.uk
nationaltrust.org.uk/overbecks

Overbeck's Garden offers views over the Salcombe Estuary and winding paths to explore

Parke

near Bovey Tracey, Devon

1974 [icon]

Historic Parke in Devon, top and above

On the south-eastern edge of Dartmoor sits this historic parkland, rich in wildlife. The Wray Valley cycle trail runs along the old railway line, and paths follow the course of the River Bovey meandering through woodlands and meadows. Look out for the walled garden and historic orchard. **Satnav**: use TQ13 9JQ.

Access: [icons]

Find out more: 01647 433306 or parke@nationaltrust.org.uk
nationaltrust.org.uk/parke

Plymbridge Woods

near Plymouth, Devon

1968

The wooded valley of the River Plym creates a link from the edge of Plymouth to the heights of Dartmoor. Footpaths lead through woodlands and alongside industrial ruins. There's also a family-friendly cycle path (NCN27) along an old railway line, a wooded mountain-bike trail and a variety of running routes. **Satnav**: use PL7 4SR for Plymbridge.

Access:

Find out more: 01752 341377 or plymbridgewoods@nationaltrust.org.uk
nationaltrust.org.uk/plymbridge-woods

The River Plym at Plymbridge Woods in Devon

Ringstead Bay

on the Jurassic Coast,
near Weymouth, Dorset

1949

The shingle beach at Ringstead Bay in Dorset

This quiet, unspoilt stretch of the Jurassic Coast in West Dorset is like the seaside of childhood memories: a perfect sweep of shingle beach with rock pools inviting you to explore, backed by farmland and cliffs covered with flowers and butterflies. The seawater is incredibly clear and safe for bathing. **Satnav**: use DT2 8NQ for Southdown.

Find out more: 01297 489481 or ringsteadbay@nationaltrust.org.uk
nationaltrust.org.uk/ringstead-bay

Saltram

near Plymouth, Devon

1957 🏛️ ❀ ⚓

High above the River Plym, with magnificent views across the estuary, Saltram's rolling landscape parkland now provides wooded walks and open space for rest and play on Plymouth's outskirts. Saltram was home to the Parker family from 1743 and the house reflects their increasingly prominent lifestyle during the Georgian period. The magnificent decoration and original contents include Robert Adam's Neo-classical Saloon, original Chinese wallpapers, 18th-century oriental, European and English ceramics and a superb country-house library. Outside, the garden's planting offers something of interest all year, and there are also follies and an 18th-century orangery to explore. **Satnav**: enter Romilly Gardens, not postcode (look for Saltram sign).

Access: 🅿️ 🚪 🎨 🚽 ♿ ♿

Find out more: 01752 333500 or saltram@nationaltrust.org.uk   Plympton, near Plymouth, Devon PL7 1UH
nationaltrust.org.uk/saltram

Saltram in Devon: clockwise from above, the magnificent house, Robert Adam's Neo-classical Saloon and outdoor fun

Devon and Dorset

Shaugh Bridge

on Dartmoor, near Shaugh Prior,
Devon 1960

Ancient oakwoods and mossy boulders
cloak the Plym Valley; riverside walks pass
the atmospheric Dewerstone Rocks and
industrial ruins. **Note**: watch out for
climbers on the Dewerstone Rocks.
Satnav: use PL7 5HD.

Find out more:
shaughbridge@nationaltrust.org.uk
nationaltrust.org.uk/shaugh-bridge

South Milton Sands

Thurlestone, near Kingsbridge, Devon

1980

This popular beach – a long sweep of
golden sand and rock pools – edges a
sheltered bay of crystal-clear water and
looks out to the iconic Thurlestone Rock
offshore. The nearby wetland is home to
many bird species and is an ideal place
to spot rare migratory visitors.
Satnav: use TQ7 3JY.

Thurlestone Rock in Devon

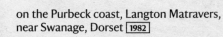

South Milton Sands boasts crystal-clear water

Access:

Find out more: 01752 346585 or
southmiltonsands@nationaltrust.org.uk
nationaltrust.org.uk/south-milton-sands

Spyway

on the Purbeck coast, Langton Matravers,
near Swanage, Dorset 1982

Gateway to Dancing Ledge and a dramatic
coast of grassy clifftops teeming with
wildlife. Fabulous walking – some steep
slopes. **Note**: sorry no toilet.
Satnav: use BH19 3HG.

Find out more: 01929 450002 or
spyway@nationaltrust.org.uk
nationaltrust.org.uk/spyway

Studland Bay

Studland, near Swanage, Dorset

1982

This glorious slice of Purbeck coastline is famed for its 4-mile stretch of golden sand, gently shelving bathing waters and views of Old Harry Rocks and the Isle of Wight. With four beaches to choose from, Studland is loved by young families and watersports fans of all ages, and it includes the most popular naturist beach in Britain. The vast swathe of heathland behind the beach is a haven for native wildlife and features all six British reptiles. Footpaths and bridleways through sand dunes, woods and wild open landscape encourage you to explore. Wildlife to spot includes deer, insects and

Studland Bay, Dorset: four miles of golden sand and four beaches to choose from

birds, as well as numerous wild flowers. Studland was the inspiration for Toytown in Enid Blyton's *Noddy*. **Note**: toilets at Shell Bay, Knoll Beach and Middle Beach; also South Beach (not National Trust). **Satnav**: use BH19 3AQ for Knoll Beach.

Access: 🅿️♿🚻♿

Find out more: 01929 450500 or studlandbay@nationaltrust.org.uk
nationaltrust.org.uk/studland

Walking and watersports at Studland Bay, below and bottom

Watersmeet

on Exmoor, near Lynmouth, Devon

1955   🏠🏛️🚸🌲

Watersmeet, Devon, is a haven for wildlife

This area, where the lush valleys of the East Lyn and Hoar Oak Water meet the high open moorland of Kipscombe, is a haven for wildlife and offers excellent walking. At the heart sits Watersmeet House, a 19th-century fishing lodge, which is now a tea garden. **Note**: deep gorge with steep walk down to house. **Satnav**: use EX35 6NT.

Access: ♿🚻

Find out more: 01598 752648 or watersmeet@nationaltrust.org.uk
nationaltrust.org.uk/watersmeet

Wembury

near Plymouth, Devon

1939

A great beach, and more: some of the best rock pools in the country, good surfing, masses of wildlife and views of a distinctive island – the Great Mewstone. Starting point for lovely coastal walks to Wembury Point and the Yealm Estuary. **Note**: toilet (not National Trust). **Satnav**: use PL9 0HP.

Access:

Find out more: 01752 346585. 01752 862538 (Marine Centre) or wembury@nationaltrust.org.uk
nationaltrust.org.uk/wembury

Making sandcastles on Wembury Beach with the Great Mewstone in the background

The beach at Wembury in Devon

White Mill

Sturminster Marshall, near Wimborne Minster, Dorset BH21 4BX 1982

This 18th-century corn mill with original wooden machinery is built on a Domesday Book site in a peaceful riverside setting.

Find out more: 01258 858051 or whitemill@nationaltrust.org.uk
nationaltrust.org.uk/white-mill

Woolacombe

near Ilfracombe, Devon 1935

A golden beach and huge dunes, amazing surfing, perfect coves for rock-pooling and numerous headland walks with views of Lundy. **Satnav**: use EX34 7BG.

Find out more: 01271 870555 or woolacombe@nationaltrust.org.uk
nationaltrust.org.uk/woolacombe

Herbaceous borders dwarf two young
visitors at Tyntesfield, North Somerset.
Competition entry from Edward Gorochowski

Somerset and
Wiltshire

Buildings and/or gardens

Entry points to coast and countryside

National Trust land

Places in neighbouring counties

Devon and Dorset, page 46

The Cotswolds, Buckinghamshire and Oxfordshire, page 106

Berkshire, Hampshire and the Isle of Wight, page 132

10 miles

To discover more coastal and countryside car parks in Somerset and Wiltshire, go to nationaltrust.org.uk/carparks

Bossington
Homer Wood
Webber's Post
Selworthy
Minehead
Dunster Castle
Coleridge Cottage
Fyne Court
TAUNTON
Bridgwater
M5
Wellington Monument
Knightshayes
Tiverton
Killerton
M5
Barrington Court
Stoke-sub-Hamdon Priory
Montacute House
Treasurer's House
Priest's House
Yeovil
Tintinhull Garden
Lytes Cary Manor
Glastonbury Tor
Wells
Cheddar Gorge
King John's Hunting Lodge
Brean Down
Sand Point
Clevedon Court
Tyntesfield
BRISTOL
Blaise Hamlet
M32
M48
M4
Newark Park
Stroud
Buscot Park
Buscot and Coleshill
Cirencester
Swindon
White Horse Hill
Bath Assembly Rooms
Bath Skyline
Prior Park
Dyrham Park
Lacock
Great Chalfield Manor
The Courts Garden
Westwood Manor
Stourhead
Frome
Warminster
Devizes
Avebury
Stonehenge Landscape
SALISBURY
Dinton Park and Philipps House
Mompesson House
Mottisfont
Romsey
New Forest

Avebury

near Marlborough, Wiltshire

1943

At Avebury you'll find the largest stone circle in the world, comprising an outer stone circle and henge, the remains of two inner circles and a recently discovered square monument. The site also partially encompasses a pretty village. The Avebury landscape forms part of the Stonehenge and Avebury World Heritage Site, listed for its exceptional Neolithic and Bronze Age archaeology, and provides an ideal starting point to explore the remakable wider countryside, which contains some globally significant archaeological sites. The

The prehistoric stone circle at Avebury, Wiltshire, above and below, is the largest in the world

The garden at Avebury Manor

renowned archaeologist Alexander Keiller excavated at Avebury in the 1930s, and the Museum displays local archaeological finds and tells the story of this prehistoric landscape. Keiller's home, the 15th-century Avebury Manor with its lovely garden, is located near the Museum. **Note**: the National Trust owns and manages Avebury Stone Circle (under guardianship of English Heritage). **Satnav**: use SN8 1RD.

Access: ⓟ ⓓ 🏚 🚶 ♿

Find out more: 01672 539250 or avebury@nationaltrust.org.uk National Trust Estate Office, High Street, Avebury, Wiltshire SN8 1RD **nationaltrust.org.uk/avebury**

Barrington Court

near Ilminster, Somerset

1907 🏠 ❖ ♿

Colonel Lyle, whose family firm became part of Tate & Lyle, rescued the partially derelict 16th-century Court House in the 1920s, surrounding it with a productive estate. A keen collector of architectural salvage, Colonel Lyle filled the house with his collection of panelling, fireplaces and staircases. Now without furniture, the light, empty spaces provide atmospheric opportunities to explore their stories freely. The walled White Garden, Rose and Iris Garden and Lily Garden were influenced by Gertrude Jekyll, with playing fountains, vibrant colours and intoxicating scents. The original kitchen garden supplies the restaurant and continues the Lyle family's vision of self-sufficiency.

Barrington Court, Somerset: the Court House, below, and garden, above right

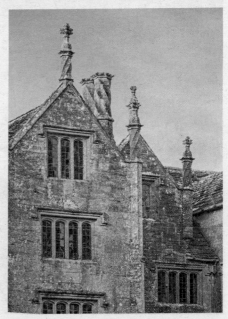

Note: independently run artisan workshops. **Satnav**: misdirects visitors to rear entrance – follow brown signs from Barrington village.

Access: [icons]

Find out more: 01460 241938 or barringtoncourt@nationaltrust.org.uk Barrington, near Ilminster, Somerset TA19 0NQ **nationaltrust.org.uk/barrington**

Bath Assembly Rooms

Bennett Street, Bath, Somerset BA1 2QH [1931]

The Assembly Rooms were at the heart of fashionable Georgian society. **Note**: limited access during functions. Bath Assembly Rooms is run by Bath and North East Somerset Council.

Find out more: 01225 477789 or bathassemblyrooms@nationaltrust.org.uk **nationaltrust.org.uk/bath-assembly-rooms**

Bath Skyline

Bath, Somerset

[1959]

One of Bath's unique features, leading to its World Heritage Site designation, is its 'green setting' – encircling meadows and wooded hillsides where you can walk and relax with grandstand views over the historic cityscape. There's a 6-mile Bath Skyline waymarked walk, plus shorter routes to follow from the city centre. **Note**: sorry no toilet.

Bath Skyline, Somerset

Find out more: 01225 833977 or bathskyline@nationaltrust.org.uk **nationaltrust.org.uk/bath-skyline**

Blaise Hamlet

Henbury, Bristol BS10 7QY [1943]

Delightful hamlet of nine picturesque cottages, designed by John Nash in 1809 for Blaise Estate pensioners. **Note**: access to green only; cottages not open. Sorry no toilet.

Find out more: 01275 461900 or blaisehamlet@nationaltrust.org.uk **nationaltrust.org.uk/blaise-hamlet**

Bossington

on Exmoor, near Minehead, Somerset

1944

Walking on Bossington Hill, Somerset

Part of the Holnicote Estate, Bossington is a peaceful coastal hamlet with distinctive thatched cottages. You can race sticks from the footbridge in the woods, look for water voles or wander down to the pebble beach. There's wildlife to spot and far-reaching views to Wales and along the Exmoor coastline. **Note**: accessible facilities in the car park. **Satnav**: use TA24 8HF.

Access:

Find out more: 01643 862452 or bossington@nationaltrust.org.uk
nationaltrust.org.uk/bossington

Brean Down

near Weston-super-Mare, North Somerset

1954

One of Somerset's most striking coastal landmarks: a dramatic limestone peninsula jutting out into the Bristol Channel. You can relax on the beach at the foot of the down or take a walk along this spectacular 'natural pier' to the fort, which provides a unique insight into Brean's military past. **Note**: steep climbs and cliffs; please stay on main paths. Tide comes in quickly. **Satnav**: use TA8 2RS.

Access:

Find out more: 01278 751874 or breandown@nationaltrust.org.uk
nationaltrust.org.uk/brean-down

Brean Down, North Somerset

The dramatic peninsula at Brean Down

Cheddar Gorge

in the Mendips, near Wells, Somerset

1910

Cheddar Gorge, Somerset: a haven for wildlife

At almost 400 feet deep and 3 miles long, Cheddar is Britain's largest gorge. It was formed during successive ice ages, when glacial meltwater carved into the limestone, creating steep cliffs. The gorge is a haven for wildlife and contains many rare plants and flowers, including the Cheddar pink. **Note**: terrain is steep away from the road. Caves and car parks privately owned (charge including members). **Satnav**: use BS27 3QE.

Find out more: 01278 751874 or cheddargorge@nationaltrust.org.uk **nationaltrust.org.uk/cheddar-gorge**

Clevedon Court

Tickenham Road, Clevedon, North Somerset BS21 6QU

1961

Home to Clevedon's lords of the manor for centuries, Clevedon Court features rare domestic architecture from the medieval period and a beautiful terraced garden. The house was bought by Abraham Elton in 1709 and is still the well-loved family home of the Eltons today.

Access:

Find out more: 01275 872257 or clevedoncourt@nationaltrust.org.uk **nationaltrust.org.uk/clevedon**

Clevedon Court, North Somerset: inside the house, above, and the exterior, below

Coleridge Cottage

35 Lime Street, Nether Stowey, Bridgwater, Somerset TA5 1NQ

1909

Home to Samuel Taylor Coleridge for three years, this simple house, where he wrote his best-known poems, was the birthplace of literary Romanticism. You can immerse yourself in 18th-century sights and sounds, and Coleridge's poetry comes to life in the cottage and wildflower garden.

Access:

Find out more: 01278 732662 or coleridgecottage@nationaltrust.org.uk
nationaltrust.org.uk/coleridge-cottage

Coleridge Cottage, Somerset, is the birthplace of literary Romanticism

The Courts Garden

Holt, near Bradford on Avon, Wiltshire BA14 6RR

1943

This curious English country garden is a hidden gem. Garden rooms of different styles, shaped by the vision of past owners and gardeners, reveal themselves at every turn. You'll find herbaceous borders, topiary, a peaceful water garden, statuary, an arboretum, kitchen garden, naturally planted spring bulbs and a sunken garden.

Access:

Find out more: 01225 782875 or courtsgarden@nationaltrust.org.uk
nationaltrust.org.uk/courts-garden

Dinton Park and Philipps House

Dinton, Salisbury, Wiltshire SP3 5HH 1943

Tranquil rolling parkland, perfect for walks and picnics, surrounds a neo-Grecian house designed by Jeffry Wyatville in 1820.
Note: the house is closed; however, the park is open daily. Sorry no toilet.

Find out more: 01672 539920 or dintonpark@nationaltrust.org.uk
nationaltrust.org.uk/dinton-park-and-philipps-house

Dunster Castle and Watermill

Dunster, near Minehead,
Somerset TA24 6SL

1976

Dramatically sited on top of a wooded hill, a castle has existed here since at least Norman times. Its impressive medieval gatehouse and ruined Bastion Tower are a reminder of its turbulent history. The castle that you see today, home to the Luttrell family for over 600 years, became an elegant country home during the 19th century and features ornate plaster ceilings and rare 17th-century leather hangings. The terraced garden displays varieties of Mediterranean and subtropical plants, while the tranquil riverside wooded garden

Dunster Castle and Watermill in Somerset: the dramatic castle, above, and grounds, below

below, with its natural play area, leads to the surviving 18th-century working watermill. There are panoramic views from the castle and grounds of the surrounding Exmoor countryside and over the Bristol Channel towards Wales.

Access: 🅿🚻♿🦽🦼

Find out more: 01643 823004 (Infoline). 01643 821314 or dunstercastle@nationaltrust.org.uk
nationaltrust.org.uk/dunster

Dunster, inside and out, offers so much for visitors to discover, whatever their age

Fyne Court

near Bridgwater, Somerset

1967 🏠♿♻🦽🦼

This is a hidden gem in the Quantock Hills. While the house (former home of amateur scientist Andrew Crosse) no longer stands, the site remains simply beautiful within its woods and meadows. A great place for gentle walks, splashing in streams, building dens and discovering ruins. **Satnav**: use TA5 2EQ.

Access: 🅿🚻♿🦼

Find out more: 01823 451587 or fynecourt@nationaltrust.org.uk
nationaltrust.org.uk/fyne-court

Glastonbury Tor

near Glastonbury, Somerset 1933

Iconic tor topped by a 15th-century tower, with spectacular views over the Somerset Levels, Dorset and Wiltshire. **Note**: sorry no toilet. **Satnav**: use BA6 8DB for nearest free parking.

Find out more: 01278 751874 or glastonburytor@nationaltrust.org.uk
nationaltrust.org.uk/glastonbury

Great Chalfield Manor and Garden

near Melksham, Wiltshire SN12 8NH

1943 | 🏠 ✝ ❖ ♨

A monkey, soldiers and griffins adorn the rooftops of this moated medieval manor, looking over the terraces of the romantic garden with topiary houses, rose garden and spring-fed fishpond. All is lovingly looked after by the Floyd family. The manor has featured in several television dramas, including *Wolf Hall*. **Note**: home to the donor family tenants, who manage it for the National Trust.

Access: 🅿️ 🅳 🆎 📶

Find out more: 01225 782239 or greatchalfieldmanor@nationaltrust.org.uk
nationaltrust.org.uk/great-chalfield

Great Chalfield Manor and Garden in Wiltshire, below

Horner Wood

on Exmoor, near Minehead, Somerset

1944 | 🏠 ♨ 🐾

One of the largest and most beautiful ancient oak woods in Britain, Horner Wood (above) is part of the Holnicote Estate. 324 hectares (800 acres) of woodland clothe the lower slopes of surrounding moorland, following river and stream valleys. This National Nature Reserve is home to a rich variety of wildlife. **Note**: toilets in car park. **Satnav**: use TA24 8HY.

Find out more: 01643 862452 or hornerwood@nationaltrust.org.uk
nationaltrust.org.uk/horner-wood

King John's Hunting Lodge

The Square, Axbridge, Somerset BS26 2AP 1968

This early Tudor timber-framed wool merchant's house (dating from around 1500) provides a fascinating insight into local history. **Note**: run as a local history museum by Axbridge and District Museum Trust.

Find out more: 01934 732012 or kingjohns@nationaltrust.org.uk
nationaltrust.org.uk/king-johns-hunting-lodge

Lacock

near Chippenham, Wiltshire

1944 🏠✝♣♨

You can see why Ela of Salisbury chose this spot for her abbey in 1232: nestled alongside the River Avon in a rolling Wiltshire landscape, Lacock invites you to stay. The abbey reveals evidence of a legacy of almost 800 years of past owners with sophisticated taste, who sensitively turned it from a nunnery into an unusual family home, furnished with well-loved mementoes and furniture. Seasonal colour can be discovered in the wooded grounds, Botanic Garden, greenhouse and orchard. The Fox Talbot Museum celebrates William Henry Fox Talbot, who created the first photographic negative and established this as a birthplace of photography. Lacock has a homely feel and the village, with its timber-framed cottages, remains a bustling community.

Lacock in Wiltshire, this page and opposite, offers an unusual home, as well as a museum, garden and grounds to explore

Note: abbey winter opening arrangements are limited. **Satnav**: may direct down closed road. Set to Hither Way, Lacock, for car park.

Access: 🅿️🅳♿🚻♿♿

Find out more: 01249 730459 or lacock@nationaltrust.org.uk   Lacock, near Chippenham, Wiltshire SN15 2LG **nationaltrust.org.uk/lacock**

Somerset and Wiltshire

Lytes Cary Manor

near Somerton, Somerset TA11 7HU

1949 🏠✝❀♣

This intimate medieval manor house was originally home to the Lyte family, who lived here for several generations until the 18th century. After years of neglect, Lytes Cary was lovingly restored in the early 20th century by Sir Walter Jenner and his wife, Lady Flora, and is arranged as it was in their time. A stroll around the Arts and Crafts-inspired garden beside the house reveals garden rooms, divided by high yew hedges, collections of topiary, sensuous herbaceous borders, orchards and manicured lawns. The Manor is surrounded by fertile farmland, wild meadows, woodland and flood plains. **Note**: access to parts of the garden may be restricted to preserve the grass.

Access: 🅿♿🚻♿

Find out more: 01458 224471 or lytescarymanor@nationaltrust.org.uk
nationaltrust.org.uk/lytes-cary-manor

Lovingly restored Lytes Cary Manor in Somerset, above and below

Mompesson House

The Close, Salisbury, Wiltshire SP1 2EL

1952

Visiting Salisbury's Cathedral Close, you step back into a past world. As you enter Mompesson House, featured in the film *Sense and Sensibility*, the feeling of leaving the modern world behind deepens. The tranquil atmosphere is enhanced by the magnificent plasterwork, graceful oak staircase and fine period furniture, which are the main features of this perfectly proportioned Queen Anne town house. Mompesson House has one of the finest displays of English 18th-century drinking glasses and a collection of stumpwork, a fascinating example of raised embroidery. The garden, with traditional herbaceous borders and pergola, is an oasis of calm in Salisbury.

Access:

Find out more: 01722 335659 or mompessonhouse@nationaltrust.org.uk
nationaltrust.org.uk/mompesson-house

Leave the modern world behind at tranquil Mompesson House in Salisbury, Wiltshire, above and below

Montacute House

Montacute, Somerset TA15 6XP

1931

This architecturally daring Elizabethan mansion was built to flaunt both wealth and power. Today its glittering façade shelters nationally important collections of furniture and textiles: 500-year-old tapestries exquisitely worked with heroes, saints, fishes and flowers; samplers touchingly stitched by little fingers; and more than 50 portraits on loan from the National Portrait Gallery. Outside, you can walk in Elizabethan footsteps through a formal garden, broken by cloud-pruned hedges and Victorian floral profusion. Wide lawns create open spaces, while avenues of trees lead you out into parkland, bluebell woods and a former motte-and-bailey castle now topped by an 18th-century folly.

Access:

Find out more: 01935 823289 or montacute@nationaltrust.org.uk **nationaltrust.org.uk/montacute-house**

Montacute House in Somerset, above and below, was built to flaunt wealth and power

Priest's House, Muchelney

Muchelney, Langport, Somerset TA10 0DQ 1911

Medieval hall-house, built in 1308. **Note:** private home. Sorry no toilet. **Satnav:** use TA10 0DQ.

Find out more: 01935 823289 or priestshouse@nationaltrust.org.uk **nationaltrust.org.uk/priests-house-muchelney**

Prior Park Landscape Garden

Ralph Allen Drive, Bath, Somerset BA2 5AH

1993 ✤

Perched on a hillside overlooking Bath, this elevated spot was chosen by Ralph Allen to show off his estate to the city. The magical landscape garden that he created captures a moment in time: 1764, the year of Allen's death. There is a lot to discover, including winding paths leading to hidden retreats, dramatic views over Bath and a rare Palladian Bridge. The major restoration project to repair the 18th-century dams finishes in 2021, with replanting around the lakes to follow. Access to the lakes

Exploring Prior Park Landscape Garden in Bath, Somerset, above and below left

may be restricted, but you'll have a once-in-a-lifetime opportunity to see the work in progress. **Note**: steep slopes, steps, uneven paths. House not accessible (not National Trust).

Access: 🚻 ♿

Find out more: 01225 833977 or priorpark@nationaltrust.org.uk
nationaltrust.org.uk/prior-park

Sand Point

near Kewstoke, North Somerset 1964

A natural pier into the Bristol Channel, north of Weston-super-Mare and Brean Down. Perfect for picnics; views across Sand Bay. **Note**: steep climbs and cliffs – please stay on main paths. Tide comes in quickly. Sorry, no toilets. **Satnav**: use BS22 9UD.

Find out more: 01278 751874 or sandpoint@nationaltrust.org.uk
nationaltrust.org.uk/sand-point

Selworthy

on Exmoor, near Minehead, Somerset

1944 ✚ 🏛 👤

Selworthy is a good place to start discovering the wonderfully varied Exmoor landscapes within the 4,856-hectare (12,500-acre) Holnicote Estate. This is a timeless rural landscape of thatched cottages, a medieval church, woodland walks and sweeping views across the vale (above) to Dunkery Beacon, Exmoor's highest point. **Satnav**: use TA24 8TP.

Find out more: 01643 862452 or selworthy@nationaltrust.org.uk
nationaltrust.org.uk/selworthy

Stoke-sub-Hamdon Priory

North Street, Stoke-sub-Hamdon, Somerset TA14 6QP 1946

Fascinating small complex of buildings, formerly the home of priests serving the Chapel of St Nicholas (now destroyed). **Note**: sorry no toilet. Please respect the privacy of tenants in the main house.

Find out more: 01935 823289 or stokehamdonpriory@nationaltrust.org.uk
nationaltrust.org.uk/stoke-sub-hamdon-priory

Stonehenge Landscape

near Amesbury, Wiltshire

1927 🏛 👤

You can wander freely through thousands of acres of downland within the Stonehenge and Avebury World Heritage Site. The landscape around the famous stones is studded with ancient monuments, such as the Avenue and Cursus, and abounds with wildlife. The visitor centre shuttle stops at Fargo woodland on request. **Note**: English Heritage manages stone circle, visitor centre/car park. Bookings via english-heritage.org.uk. Pay and display car park free to Trust members (booking essential). Trust members enter free (excluding International National Trust or affiliate membership organisation members). **Satnav**: use SP3 4DX.

Stonehenge Landscape in Wiltshire

Access: 🅿♿ 🚻

Find out more: 0370 333 1181 (English Heritage). 01672 539920 (National Trust) or stonehenge@nationaltrust.org.uk
nationaltrust.org.uk/stonehenge-landscape

The landscape garden at Stourhead
in Wiltshire, above and below

Stourhead

near Mere, Wiltshire BA12 6QF

1946 🏛➕🏠❀⚓

'A living work of art' is how Stourhead was described when it first opened nearly 300 years ago. The world-famous landscape garden surrounds a glistening lake. There are towering trees, exotic rhododendrons, classical temples and a magical grotto to explore. The house at Stourhead was one of the first in the country to showcase Palladian architecture. With a unique Regency library, Chippendale furniture

and inspirational paintings, this was a grand family home, shaped by generations of the Hoare family. Outside, views stretch across the countryside, and the lawns are perfect for picnics. Great for walking and wildlife spotting, with 1,072 hectares (2,650 acres) of chalk downs, ancient woods, Iron Age hill forts and farmland to explore.

Access: 🅿️ 🚾 ♿

Find out more: 01747 841152 or stourhead@nationaltrust.org.uk
nationaltrust.org.uk/stourhead

Discovering the Palladian house at Stourhead, above, and a wet walk by the lake, below

Tintinhull Garden

Farm Street, Tintinhull, Yeovil, Somerset BA22 8PZ

1953 ❖

The vision of Phyllis Reiss, amateur gardener, lives on in this small yet perfectly formed garden, with 'living rooms' of colour and scent. Created in the last century around a 17th-century manor house, it's one of the most harmonious small gardens in Britain, featuring secluded lawns, pools and imaginative borders.

Access: 🅿️ 🚾 ♿

Find out more: 01458 224471 or tintinhull@nationaltrust.org.uk
nationaltrust.org.uk/tintinhull

Treasurer's House, Martock

Martock, Somerset TA12 6JL 1971

Completed in 1293, this medieval house includes a Great Hall, 15th-century kitchen and an unusual wall-painting.
Note: private home. Sorry no toilet.

Find out more: 01935 823289 or treasurersmartock@nationaltrust.org.uk
nationaltrust.org.uk/treasurers-house-martock

Tyntesfield

Wraxall, Bristol, North Somerset BS48 1NX

2002

Cocooned in the Somerset countryside, Tyntesfield is a rare survivor – a near-complete Victorian Gothic country house and estate. It was created for the Gibbs family to celebrate their achievements, raise their children and share their passions for family and faith. The richly decorated house contains over 60,000 of the family's possessions, some collected by William Gibbs as he traded in the Hispanic world.

Tyntesfield, North Somerset: the richly decorated house, above, and garden, below

Tyntesfield is a rare survivor, a near-complete Victorian Gothic country house

Born in Madrid, William's story is one of long struggles with sacred debts, of young love, loss, a close-knit family and the making of a vast fortune. Today you're welcomed into this cherished place with its ornate private chapel, flower-filled terraces, towering trees, abundant kitchen garden and views across the working estate to the Somerset hills.

Access: 🅿️ ♿ 🚾 ♿ ♿ ♿

Find out more: 01275 461900 or tyntesfield@nationaltrust.org.uk
nationaltrust.org.uk/tyntesfield

Webber's Post

on Exmoor, near Minehead, Somerset 1944

Great spot for views over Horner Wood, short strolls, cycling, picnics and walking up to Dunkery Beacon, Exmoor's highest point. **Note**: sorry no toilet. **Satnav**: use TA24 8TB and follow signs to Webber's Post.

Find out more: 01643 862452 or webberspost@nationaltrust.org.uk
nationaltrust.org.uk/webbers-post

Wellington Monument

near Wellington, Somerset

1934

Standing in an informal rural setting on the edge of the Blackdown Hills, Wellington Monument – the world's tallest three-sided obelisk – has recently undergone major repairs. When you visit, you can enjoy a gentle stroll along the beech-tree avenue and savour far-reaching views across the Quantock Hills and Exmoor. **Note**: sorry no toilet. **Satnav**: use TA21 9PB.

Find out more: 01823 451587 or wellingtonmonument@nationaltrust.org.uk **nationaltrust.org.uk/wellington-monument**

Wellington Monument in Somerset

Westwood Manor

Westwood, near Bradford on Avon, Wiltshire BA15 2AF

1960

Westwood Manor in Wiltshire

Over the centuries, the residents of this small late medieval, Tudor and Jacobean house have modified the building to their own tastes, each leaving a permanent mark. The interiors are rich with decorative plasterwork, fine furniture and beautiful tapestries. Highlights are two rare keyboard instruments: a spinet and a virginal. **Note**: Westwood Manor is a family home, administered by the tenants.

Access:

Find out more: 01225 863374 or westwoodmanor@nationaltrust.org.uk **nationaltrust.org.uk/westwood-manor**

The Cotswolds, Buckinghamshire and Oxfordshire

The grand Parterre at Cliveden, Buckinghamshire, on a frosty January day

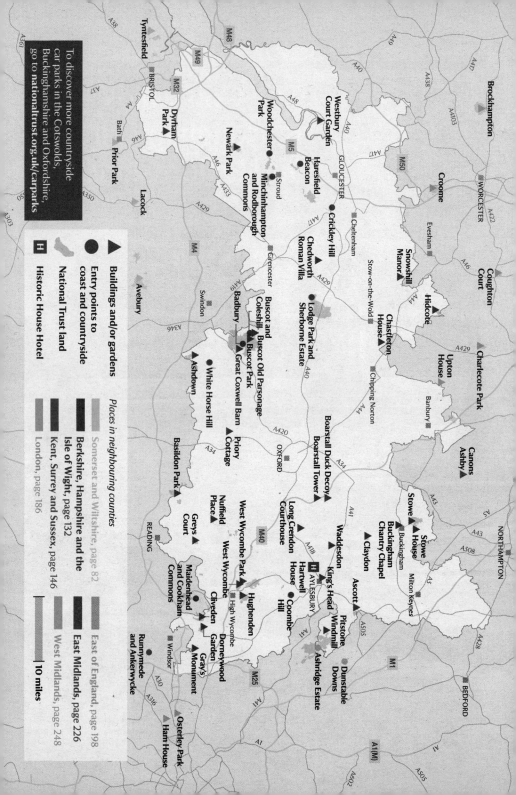

Key

Buildings and/or gardens

▲

Entry points to coast and countryside

●

National Trust land

Historic House Hotel

H

Places in neighbouring counties

Somerset and Wiltshire, page 82

Berkshire, Hampshire and the Isle of Wight, page 132

East of England, page 198

Kent, Surrey and Sussex, page 146

West Midlands, page 226

London, page 186

10 miles

Place labels

Brockhampton

Croome

Coughton Court

Canons Ashby

Charlecote Park

Upton House

Hidcote

Snowshill Manor

Chastleton House

Stowe

Stowe House

Buckingham Chantry Chapel

Claydon

Waddesdon

Ascott

Pitstone Windmill

Dunstable Downs

Ashridge Estate

King's Head

Hartwell House

Coombe Hill

Hughenden

Cliveden

Dorneywood Garden

Gray's Monument

Maidenhead and Cookham Commons

West Wycombe Park

West Wycombe

Long Crendon Courthouse

Nuffield Place

Greys Court

Boarstall Duck Decoy

Boarstall Tower

Basildon Park

Priory Cottage

Ashdown

White Horse Hill

Great Coxwell Barn

Buscot Park

Buscot Old Parsonage

Buscot and Coleshill Estate

Lodge Park and Sherborne Estate

Badbury

Chedworth Roman Villa

Crickley Hill

Haresfield Beacon

Minchinhampton and Rodborough Commons

Woodchester Park

Newark Park

Dyrham Park

Prior Park

Lacock

Tyntesfield

Westbury Court Garden

Osterley Park

Ham House

Runnymede and Ankerwycke

Ascott

Wing, near Leighton Buzzard,
Buckinghamshire LU7 0PP

 1949

16th-century Ascott in Buckinghamshire

Ascott House, an 'Old English'
half-timbered manor, dates back to
the 16th century. It was transformed
by the Rothschilds towards the end
of the 19th century and houses several
exceptional collections. The extensive
gardens are an attractive mix of formal
and natural, with specimen trees, shrubs
and beautiful herbaceous borders.
Note: Ascott is a family home,
administered by the de Rothschild family.

Access:

Find out more: 01296 688242 or
ascott@nationaltrust.org.uk
nationaltrust.org.uk/ascott

Ashdown

Lambourn, Newbury, Oxfordshire RG17 8RE

1956

Unique 17th-century chalk-block hunting
lodge, with doll's-house appearance, built
for the Queen of Bohemia by the Earl of
Craven, set in a historic woodland. Come
and learn about this family's intriguing
history, and discover the fine 17th-century
paintings which hang alongside the
staircase. Outstanding rooftop views across
three counties. **Note**: access to roof via
100-step staircase. **Satnav**: from B4000
follow local brown signs.

Access:

Find out more: 01793 762209 or
ashdown@nationaltrust.org.uk
nationaltrust.org.uk/ashdown

**Doll's-house-like, Ashdown in Oxfordshire
was built for the Queen of Bohemia**

Badbury

Coleshill, near Swindon

2011

A tempting walk winds through a bluebell glade at Badbury, near Swindon

This former plantation woodland is criss-crossed with easy circular walks, offering stunning views over the Upper Thames Valley. A spread of snowdrops heralds spring, followed by a carpet of bluebells. A copse of military-straight beech trees defines the Iron Age hill fort. **Note**: sorry no toilet. **Satnav**: use SN7 7NJ (does not take you directly to car park).

Find out more: 01793 762209 or badbury@nationaltrust.org.uk **nationaltrust.org.uk/badbury**

Boarstall Duck Decoy

Boarstall, near Bicester, Buckinghamshire HP18 9UX 1980

One of the last remaining decoys in the country, a fascinating insight into rural life, with a peaceful woodland walk.

Find out more: 01280 817156 or boarstalldecoy@nationaltrust.org.uk **nationaltrust.org.uk/boarstall-duck-decoy**

Boarstall Tower

Boarstall, near Bicester, Buckinghamshire HP18 9UX 1943

Charming 14th-century moated gatehouse set in beautiful gardens, retaining original fortified appearance. Grade I listed. **Note**: upper levels access via spiral staircase. Approach paths not suitable for wheelchairs.

Find out more: 01280 817156 or boarstalltower@nationaltrust.org.uk **nationaltrust.org.uk/boarstall-tower**

Buckingham Chantry Chapel

Market Hill, Buckingham, Buckinghamshire MK18 1JX 1912

Atmospheric 15th-century chapel, restored by Sir Gilbert Scott in 1875, in the heart of Buckingham.

Find out more: 01280 817156 or buckinghamchantry@nationaltrust.org.uk **nationaltrust.org.uk/buckingham-chantry-chapel**

The Buscot and Coleshill Estates

Coleshill, near Swindon

1956

These countryside estates (above) on the western border of Oxfordshire include the attractive, unspoilt villages of Buscot and Coleshill, each with a thriving tea-room. There are circular walks of differing lengths and a series of footpaths criss-crossing the estates, with breathtaking countryside and wildlife at Buscot Lock and Badbury Hill. **Note**: toilets at the Old Carpenters Yard in Coleshill, outside the estate office and in Buscot. **Satnav**: use SN6 7PT.

Find out more: 01793 762209 or buscotandcoleshill@nationaltrust.org.uk
nationaltrust.org.uk/buscot-coleshill-estates

Buscot Old Parsonage

Buscot, Faringdon, Oxfordshire SN7 8DQ
1949

Beautiful early 18th-century house with small walled garden, on the banks of the Thames. **Note**: sorry no toilet.

Find out more: 01793 762209 or buscot@nationaltrust.org.uk
nationaltrust.org.uk/buscot-old-parsonage

Buscot Park

Faringdon, Oxfordshire SN7 8BU

1949

Lord Faringdon's family live in the house, maintain the interior, manage the grounds, gardens and tea-room, and are responsible for the public display of the contents owned by The Faringdon Collection Trust. This unusual arrangement with the National Trust breathes life into the property and gives it an individualistic air.

Access:

Find out more: 01367 240932 (Infoline). 01367 240786 or buscotpark@nationaltrust.org.uk
nationaltrust.org.uk/buscot-park

Buscot Park, Oxfordshire: wisteria-clad archway

Chastleton House

near Moreton-in-Marsh, Oxfordshire

1991

Within the warm, weathered Cotswold stone walls of this ancient country house lie faded elegant interiors full of myths and memories – a compelling time capsule of 400 years of family life. Discover the secrets they hide, then explore the garden, a sleeping beauty preserved in graceful decline.
Note: house is challenging for the less able. **Satnav**: use GL56 0SP to the Greedy Goose pub, then follow brown signs.

Access:

Find out more: 01494 755560 (Infoline). 01608 674355 or chastleton@nationaltrust.org.uk Chastleton, near Moreton-in-Marsh, Oxfordshire GL56 0SU
nationaltrust.org.uk/chastleton

Chastleton House, Oxfordshire: faded elegance

Chedworth Roman Villa

Yanworth, near Cheltenham, Gloucestershire GL54 3LJ

1924

Cradled in a beautiful wooded valley and fed by a natural spring, this high-status Roman villa saw imperial fashions and local spirits living side by side. Nature took over and hid the magnificent mosaics, intricate hypocaust systems, bathhouses and ancient water-shrine for more than 1,500 years until Victorian gamekeepers rediscovered the site. The National Trust has, in turn, looked after Chedworth's Roman treasures and Victorian legacy for nearly a century, providing its modern villa guests with new facilities, as well as astonishing archaeology, to enjoy. It remains a hidden place of natural beauty and continual discovery.

Access: 🅿️🅳️ᴸᵂᶜ♪♿

Find out more: 01242 890256 or chedworth@nationaltrust.org.uk
nationaltrust.org.uk/chedworth

Chedworth Roman Villa in Gloucestershire, left, is home to historic mosaics, below

Claydon

Middle Claydon, near Buckingham, Buckinghamshire MK18 2EY

 1956 🏠✝️❀⛴️

The simple Georgian exterior of Claydon, Buckinghamshire, hides lavish interiors

Nestled in peaceful parkland, the simple Georgian exterior hides a lavish interior showcasing every 18th-century style imaginable, from Palladian and Neo-classical to chinoiserie and Gothick fantasy, with exceptional Rococo carvings. Florence Nightingale had her own rooms at Claydon, spending many summers looking out over the lakes and medieval church. **Note**: Claydon Courtyard (not National Trust).

Access: 🅿️🅳️ᴸᵂᶜ♪♿

Find out more: 01296 730349 or claydon@nationaltrust.org.uk
nationaltrust.org.uk/claydon

Cliveden

near Maidenhead, Buckinghamshire

1942 🏠 ♣ 🏊

A majestic vision set high above the
Thames, Cliveden is a proud celebration
of status and splendour, where the charms
of art and nature join. Six powerful families
have embellished and enhanced Cliveden's
history over the course of 350 years. Each
family added their own extravagant touch,
creating a series of distinctive and
delightful gardens. You can discover
vibrant floral displays at the grand Parterre,
satisfying symmetry in the Long Garden,
the tranquil intimacy of the Rose Garden
and rich autumn colour within the oriental
Water Garden. The tree-lined avenue of
the Green Drive is the spine of the estate,
acting as a gateway to the miles of
footpaths that meander through the
majestic woodlands and along the riverbank.

Coombe Hill

Butler's Cross, near Wendover, Buckinghamshire 1918

Nationally important chalk grassland site and the highest viewpoint in the Chilterns with stunning views over the Aylesbury Vale.
Note: sorry no toilet.
Satnav: use HP17 0UR.

Find out more: 01494 755573 or coombehill@nationaltrust.org.uk

Crickley Hill

Birdlip, Gloucestershire 1935

Sitting high on the Cotswold escarpment with views towards the Welsh hills, Crickley Hill overlooks Gloucester and Cheltenham.
Satnav: use GL4 8JY.

Find out more: 01452 814213 or crickleyhill@nationaltrust.org.uk
nationaltrust.org.uk/crickley-hill

The glorious gardens at Cliveden in Buckinghamshire, this page and left

Note: overnight mooring available on Cliveden Reach, does not include entry.
Satnav: for gardens use Cliveden Road and SL1 8NS; for woodlands use SL6 0HJ.

Access: 🅿🚌🚻♿

Find out more: 01628 605069 or cliveden@nationaltrust.org.uk
Cliveden Road, Taplow, Maidenhead, Buckinghamshire SL1 8NS
nationaltrust.org.uk/cliveden

Dorneywood Garden

Dorneywood, Dorney Wood Road, Burnham, Buckinghamshire SL1 8PY 1942

Ministerial residence since 1954 with country garden. Teas. Open selected afternoons (dates may change at short notice). **Note**: no photography. Visitor details recorded for security reasons.

Find out more:
dorneywood@nationaltrust.org.uk
nationaltrust.org.uk/dorneywood

The house and garden at Dyrham Park, near Bath, South Gloucestershire

See how you've helped, and what more you can do: nationaltrust.org.uk/donate

Dyrham Park

Dyrham, near Bath,
South Gloucestershire SN14 8HY

1961 ▦✝✿♦

Dyrham Park is a place of exploration.
Outdoor adventurers can savour the
far-reaching views towards the Welsh hills
from the 109 hectares (270 acres) of
ancient parkland. For inspiration and
tranquillity, you can wander round the
ever-changing garden. Sumptuous planting
in the Pool Garden contrasts with the
formality of The Avenue, set against the
peaceful wooded terraces. In the house
you'll be able to get a taste of the 17th
century, with a collection of objects and art
revealing the personal passions of William
Blathwayt – Secretary at War to King
William III and Auditor General of
Plantation Revenues. Dyrham's colonial
connections are explored through an
exhibition, including contemporary
responses. **Satnav**: enter via A46.

**Discovering the parkland of Dyrham Park,
below, and admiring vivid blooms, above right**

Access: ▣▣▣♿

Find out more: 0117 937 2501 or
dyrhampark@nationaltrust.org.uk
nationaltrust.org.uk/dyrham-park

Gray's Monument

Stoke Poges, Buckinghamshire
SL2 4NZ 1925

This 5-metre-high monument, surrounded
by expansive parkland views, captures the
poet Thomas Gray's long association with
the village. **Note**: sorry no toilet.
Satnav: use SL2 4NZ.

Find out more: 01628 605069 (Cliveden) or
graysmonument@nationaltrust.org.uk

Great Coxwell Barn

Great Coxwell, Faringdon,
Oxfordshire SN7 7LZ 1956

Former 13th-century monastic barn, a
favourite of William Morris, who would
regularly bring his guests to wonder at its
structure. **Note**: sorry no toilet; narrow
access lanes leading to property.

Find out more: 01793 762209 or
greatcoxwellbarn@nationaltrust.org.uk
nationaltrust.org.uk/great-coxwell-barn

Greys Court

Rotherfield Greys, Henley-on-Thames,
Oxfordshire RG9 4PG

1969 🏠 ✿ ♨

Set in the rolling hills of the Chilterns, Greys
Court is a picturesque Tudor manor house
surrounded by layers of history, intimate
walled gardens and glorious wooded
parkland. The house is warm and
welcoming, unfurling the memories of the
Brunner family through the rooms of their
comfortable home. Across the perfect lawn,
a medieval tower and patchwork of mellow
brick buildings conceal an English country
garden. Through an ancient arch, seasonal
blooms are revealed, from bright bulbs
through clematis and wisteria to glorious
peonies and roses in the summer. Winter
walks in the woodland are a must.

Access: 🅿 🚻 ♿ ♿

Find out more: 01491 628529 or
greyscourt@nationaltrust.org.uk
nationaltrust.org.uk/greys-court

Warm and welcoming Greys Court in Oxfordshire sits within glorious wooded parkland

Haresfield Beacon

near Stroud, Gloucestershire

1931

High on three spurs of the Cotswold escarpment with views towards the Brecon Beacons. Abundant wildlife and a wealth of archaeological features to discover, including long and round barrows, a hill fort and cross dyke.

Haresfield Beacon in Gloucestershire, above and below

Satnav: use GL6 6PP for Shortwood car park.

Find out more: 01452 814213 or haresfieldbeacon@nationaltrust.org.uk
nationaltrust.org.uk/haresfield-beacon

Hartwell House and Spa

Oxford Road, near Aylesbury, Buckinghamshire HP17 8NR

2008

Elegant Grade I-listed stately home, with both Jacobean and Georgian façades, magnificent Great Hall, with exceptional ceiling, and elegant drawing rooms. Set in beautifully landscaped grounds, including ruined Gothick church, lake, bridge and 36 hectares (90 acres) of parkland. One hour from central London. **Note**: access is for hotel guests only, including for luncheon, afternoon tea and dinner. Children over six welcome. Held on a long lease from the Ernest Cook Trust.

Find out more: 01296 747444 or info@hartwell-house.com
hartwell-house.com

Hidcote

near Chipping Campden, Gloucestershire

1948 ▓

This world-famous Arts and Crafts-inspired garden is nestled in a north Cotswolds hamlet. Created by the talented horticulturist Major Lawrence Johnston, Hidcote's colourful and intricately designed outdoor spaces are full of surprises, which change in harmony with the seasons. Many of the unusual plants found growing in the garden were collected from Johnston's plant-hunting trips around the world. Wandering along the narrow pathways, you come across secret gardens, unexpected views and plants that burst with colour.

Satnav: follow signs to Mickleton village and then brown signs to Hidcote.

Access: ⬚⬚⬚⬚⬚

Find out more: 01386 438333 or hidcote@nationaltrust.org.uk Hidcote Bartrim, near Chipping Campden, Gloucestershire GL55 6LR **nationaltrust.org.uk/hidcote**

The garden at Hidcote, Gloucestershire, above and below

Hughenden

High Wycombe, Buckinghamshire HP14 4LA

1947 🏛✝♣♨

It's hardly surprising that the unconventional Victorian Prime Minister Benjamin Disraeli so loved Hughenden. His handsome home, set in an unspoiled Chiltern valley with views of ancient woods and rolling hills, is full of fascinating personal memorabilia of this charismatic colourful statesman. Disraeli's country retreat later became the headquarters for a top-secret Second World War operation codenamed 'Hillside' and put Hughenden high on Hitler's target list. The Hillside

Hughenden, Buckinghamshire, below and right, Benjamin Disraeli's much-loved country retreat

exhibition and ice-house bunker bring wartime Britain to life. The estate also offers a variety of walks in the parkland and wider countryside, rewarding visitors with views of the Chiltern Hills.

Access: 🅿️ 🅳 🚾 ♿ ♿

Find out more: 01494 755565 (Infoline). 01494 755573 or hughenden@nationaltrust.org.uk
nationaltrust.org.uk/hughenden

King's Head

King's Head Passage, Market Square, Aylesbury, Buckinghamshire HP20 2RW
1925

Historic public house dating back to 1455, with a pleasant family atmosphere. This is one of England's best-preserved coaching inns. **Note**: Farmers' Bar leased by Chiltern Brewery.

Find out more: 01296 718812 (Farmers' Bar). 01280 817156 (National Trust) or kingshead@nationaltrust.org.uk
nationaltrust.org.uk/kings-head

Lodge Park and Sherborne Park Estate

near Cheltenham, Gloucestershire

 1987

Lodge Park (above) is England's only 17th-century deer-coursing grandstand. Set within a landscape designed by Charles Bridgeman and part of the Sherborne Park Estate, the grandstand was built in 1634 to satisfy John 'Crump' Dutton's love of gambling and entertaining. There are lovely walks through the Bridgeman landscape and wider estate. **Satnav**: for Lodge Park use GL54 3PP; for Sherborne Estate use GL54 3DT (Ewe Pen Barn) or GL54 3DL (Water Meadows).

Access:

Find out more: 01451 844257 or sherborneestate@nationaltrust.org.uk Aldsworth, near Cheltenham, Gloucestershire GL54 3PP **nationaltrust.org.uk/lodge-park-and-sherborne-estate**

Long Crendon Courthouse

Long Crendon, Aylesbury, Buckinghamshire HP18 9AN 1900

Superb example of a 14th-century courthouse with a wealth of local history – the second building acquired by the National Trust. **Note**: extremely steep stairs. Sorry no toilet.

Find out more: 01280 817156 or longcrendon@nationaltrust.org.uk **nationaltrust.org.uk/long-crendon-courthouse**

Minchinhampton and Rodborough Commons

near Stroud, Gloucestershire

1913

These historic Cotswold commons, traditionally grazed, are famed for rare flowers and butterflies (below), prehistoric remains and far-reaching views.

Minchinhampton Common contains a nationally important complex of Neolithic and Bronze Age burial mounds, while Rodborough Common's limestone grasslands have abundant wild flowers, including rare pasqueflowers and many varieties of orchid. **Satnav:** use GL5 5BJ for Minchinhampton; GL5 5BP for Rodborough (postcodes may be approximate).

Find out more: 01452 814213 or minchinhampton@nationaltrust.org.uk **nationaltrust.org.uk/minchinhampton**

Newark Park

Ozleworth, Wotton-under-Edge, Gloucestershire GL12 7PZ

| 1949 | 🏠🏛❄☀⚓ |

With splendid views from the Cotswold escarpment, Newark Park (above) is a secluded estate with a historic country home at its heart. From Tudor beginnings to dramatic rescue by a 20th-century Texan, the house has many stories to tell. The informal garden and estate provide space to play, explore and contemplate. **Note:** toilets in car park (additional toilets in Newark House). **Satnav:** only works when approaching from north; if approaching from south follow brown signs from Wotton-under-Edge and A46.

Access: 🅿♿♿♿♿

Find out more: 01453 842644 or newarkpark@nationaltrust.org.uk **nationaltrust.org.uk/newark-park**

Nuffield Place

Huntercombe, near Henley-on-Thames, Oxfordshire RG9 5RY

| 2011 | 🏠✷ |

Nuffield Place reveals the surprisingly down-to-earth lives of Lord Nuffield, founder of the Morris Motor Company, and his wife. Their home and personal possessions are just as they left them, the décor and furnishings intact. This intimate home exudes the tastes and interests of its remarkable owner.

Intimate Nuffield Place in Oxfordshire

Access: 🅿

Find out more: 01491 641224 or nuffieldplace@nationaltrust.org.uk **nationaltrust.org.uk/nuffield-place**

Pitstone Windmill

Ivinghoe, Buckinghamshire LU7 9EJ
1937

Believed to be the oldest postmill in
England. Stunning views of the Chilterns.
Note: access to windmill 262 yards
via a grassy field track. Steep steps.
Sorry no facilities.

Find out more: 01442 851227 or
pitstonemill@nationaltrust.org.uk
nationaltrust.org.uk/pitstone-windmill

Priory Cottage

1 Mill Street, Steventon, Abingdon,
Oxfordshire OX13 6SP 1939

Now converted into two houses, these
former monastic buildings were gifted
to the National Trust by the famous
Ferguson's Gang. **Note**: administered
by tenant. Sorry no toilet.

Find out more: 01793 762209 or
priorycottages@nationaltrust.org.uk
nationaltrust.org.uk/priory-cottage

Snowshill Manor and Garden

Snowshill, near Broadway,
Gloucestershire WR12 7JU

1951

Charles Wade was an artist and architect
who collected curious and interesting
objects that were for him a celebration of
colour, craftsmanship and design. With a

Curious treasures at Snowshill Manor and Garden,
Gloucestershire, above, and the garden, below

Stowe

Buckingham, Buckinghamshire MK18 5EQ

1989

Two views of Stowe, Buckinghamshire: lakes, follies and resident birds will keep everyone entertained

sense of fun and theatre, he took great pleasure in turning his home into a stage for these varied and sometimes unusual finds. Next to the manor house is the small cottage where Charles Wade lived. Both the manor house and cottage are surrounded by an intimate Arts and Crafts terraced garden where he created 'different courts for different moods'. **Satnav**: follow signs from centre of village.

Access: ☐☐☐

Find out more: 01386 852410 or snowshillmanor@nationaltrust.org.uk **nationaltrust.org.uk/snowshill-manor**

The beauty of Stowe has attracted visitors since 1717. Picture-perfect views, lakeside walks and temples create a monumental landscape that changes with the seasons. Full of hidden meaning and classical references, the garden remains an earthly paradise. Follow in the footsteps of 18th-century tourists by beginning your visit at the New Inn visitor centre.

The size, scale and splendour of Stowe, above and opposite, are awe-inspiring

From here it is a short walk or buggy-ride to the garden, where another world awaits. Enjoy the beauty, history and nature at Stowe, brought into perfect balance as you choose your route through the garden. The sheer size and scale are perfect for either a steady stroll or vigorous ramble, and you will leave overwhelmed by the garden's awe-inspiring splendour.

Access: 🅿️ ♿ ♿

Find out more: 01280 817156 or stowe@nationaltrust.org.uk
nationaltrust.org.uk/stowe

Stowe House

Buckingham, Buckinghamshire MK18 5EH

Stunning 18th-century house in the heart of Stowe's gardens. You can explore the restored state rooms and discover fascinating history. **Note**: operated by the Stowe House Preservation Trust. **Satnav**: use MK18 5EQ.

Find out more: 01280 818186 or stowehouse@nationaltrust.org.uk

Waddesdon

Waddesdon, near Aylesbury, Buckinghamshire HP18 0JH

 1957 🏠 ✿ 🏊

Waddesdon is a Rothschild house and gardens managed by the Rothschild Foundation. Baron Ferdinand started building the manor in 1874 to display his outstanding collection of art treasures and entertain fashionable society. His choice of a French-style château surprises many visitors. The highest quality 18th-century

Waddesdon, Buckinghamshire: the French-style château, below, and outstanding Aviary, above

Waddesdon: so many ornate interiors, above, and gardens, right, for visitors to explore

French decorative arts are displayed alongside magnificent English portraits and Dutch Old Master paintings in 40 elegant interiors. Outside is one of the finest Victorian gardens in Britain, famous for its parterre and ornate working aviary, and enhanced with classical and contemporary sculpture. Today, the manor continues its tradition of entertainment and hospitality, with events celebrating food and wine. Changing exhibitions help visitors find out more about Waddesdon's history, collections and gardens.

Access: 🅿️ ♿ 🚻 ♿ 🍴 ♿

Find out more: 01296 820414 or waddesdon@nationaltrust.org.uk
nationaltrust.org.uk/waddesdon

West Wycombe Park

West Wycombe, Buckinghamshire HP14 3AJ

1943 🏠✝🏛♿

Alongside this historic village lies an exquisite Palladian villa. This lavish home and serene landscape garden reflect the wealth and personality of its creator, the infamous Sir Francis Dashwood, founder of the Hellfire Club. Still home to the Dashwood family and their fine collection, it remains a busy, private estate. **Note**: opened in partnership with the Dashwood family. The Hellfire Caves and café are privately owned.

Access: ♿♿♿♿

Find out more: 01494 755571 (Infoline). 01494 513569 or
westwycombe@nationaltrust.org.uk
nationaltrust.org.uk/west-wycombe-park

West Wycombe Park
in Buckinghamshire

West Wycombe Village and Hill

West Wycombe, Buckinghamshire HP14 3AJ

1934 ✝♿

Historic and picturesque West Wycombe Village and Hill in Buckinghamshire

This historic village, with its many buildings of architectural interest, was an important coaching stop between London and Oxford. West Wycombe Hill offers commanding views over West Wycombe Park and the surrounding countryside. On top of the hill is St Lawrence Church with its famous golden ball. **Note**: church and mausoleum not National Trust.

Find out more: 01494 755571 (Infoline). 01494 513569 or
westwycombe@nationaltrust.org.uk
nationaltrust.org.uk/west-wycombe-park-village-and-hill

Westbury Court Garden

Westbury-on-Severn,
Gloucestershire GL14 1PD

1967

Originally laid out between 1696 and 1705,
this is the only restored Dutch water garden
in the country. There are canals, clipped
hedges, working 17th-century vegetable
plots and many old varieties of fruit trees.

Access:

Find out more: 01452 760461 or
westburycourt@nationaltrust.org.uk
**nationaltrust.org.uk/westbury-court-
garden**

Westbury Court Garden
in Gloucestershire

White Horse Hill, Oxfordshire:
this ancient landscape is
steeped in history and mythology

White Horse Hill

Uffington, Oxfordshire

1979

The White Horse at Uffington is part of an
ancient landscape, steeped in history and
mythology. It's the oldest chalk figure in the
country, dated to the late Bronze Age about
3,000 years ago. Its linear form dominates
the landscape, yet no one knows how it was
made. The walls of an Iron Age hill fort are

Woodchester Park

Nympsfield, near Stroud, Gloucestershire

1994

This tranquil wooded valley contains a 'lost landscape': remains of an 18th- and 19th-century landscape park with a chain of five lakes. The restoration of this landscape is an ongoing project. Waymarked trails (steep in places) lead through picturesque scenery, passing an unfinished Victorian mansion. **Note**: toilet not always available. Mansion managed by Woodchester Mansion Trust (not National Trust). **Satnav**: nearest GL10 3TS, then follow signs.

Find out more: 01452 814213 or woodchesterpark@nationaltrust.org.uk **nationaltrust.org.uk/woodchester**

Woodchester Park in Gloucestershire

visible on the hilltop, the highest point in Oxfordshire. You can also look down on a valley known as The Manger and a natural outcrop known as Dragon Hill, where St George was said to have fought and slain the dragon. **Note**: archaeological monuments under English Heritage guardianship. Sorry no toilet. **Satnav**: use SN7 7QJ.

Access: 🅿️♿

Find out more: 01793 762209 or whitehorsehill@nationaltrust.org.uk **nationaltrust.org.uk/white-horse-hill**

Berkshire, Hampshire and the Isle of Wight

Sunrise lights up the mansion and lake at The Vyne in Hampshire

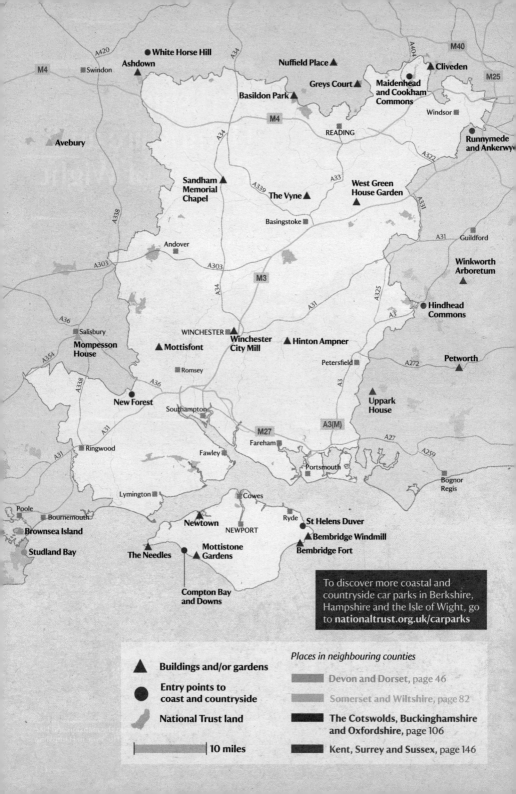

White Horse Hill ●
Ashdown ▲
Swindon ■
A420
M4
A34
Nuffield Place ▲
Greys Court ▲
Maidenhead and Cookham Commons
Cliveden ▲
M40
M404
M25
Basildon Park ▲
Windsor ■
Avebury ●
M4
READING
Runnymede and Ankerwy●
A322
A338
A34
A339
Sandham Memorial Chapel ▲
The Vyne ▲
A33
West Green House Garden ▲
A331
Basingstoke ■
Guildford ■
Andover ■
A303
A303
A34
M3
A31
A325
Winkworth Arboretum ▲
A36
Salisbury ■
WINCHESTER ■
Winchester City Mill ▲
Hindhead Commons●
A3
Mompesson House
Mottisfont ▲
Hinton Ampner ▲
Petersfield ■
A272
Petworth ▲
A354
Romsey ■
A3
A338
New Forest ●
A36
Southampton
Uppark House ▲
A31
Ringwood ■
Fawley ■
M27
A3(M)
A27
A259
Fareham ■
Portsmouth ●
Bognor Regis ■
Lymington ■
Cowes ■
Poole ●
Bournemouth ●
Newtown ▲
NEWPORT
Ryde ■
St Helens Duver ●
Brownsea Island ●
Mottistone Gardens ▲
Bembridge Windmill ▲
Bembridge Fort
Studland Bay ●
The Needles ▲
Compton Bay and Downs

To discover more coastal and countryside car parks in Berkshire, Hampshire and the Isle of Wight, go to **nationaltrust.org.uk/carparks**

▲ Buildings and/or gardens

● Entry points to coast and countryside

National Trust land

|———| 10 miles

Places in neighbouring counties

Devon and Dorset, page 46

Somerset and Wiltshire, page 82

The Cotswolds, Buckinghamshire and Oxfordshire, page 106

Kent, Surrey and Sussex, page 146

Elegant Basildon Park in Berkshire, is surrounded by historic parkland and gardens

Basildon Park

near Reading, Berkshire

1978 🏠 🎫 ♿

Sitting elegantly in 162 hectares (400 acres) of historic parkland and gardens, this 18th-century mansion was saved from destruction by Lord and Lady Iliffe in the 1950s, when it was derequisitioned after the Second World War. In a true labour of love, the Iliffes spent nearly 50 years renovating and returning the house to its former glory, acquiring a collection of fine furnishings and carefully selected Old Masters. The wooded parkland showcases glorious seasonal colour all year round, while the landscape has been restored to offer wonderful views, peaceful trails and picnic places. **Note**: entrance to main show rooms of mansion on first floor – 21 steps from ground level. **Satnav**: not reliable, please follow brown signs.

Access: 🅿️ 🅱️ 🚽 ♿

Find out more: 01491 672382 or basildonpark@nationaltrust.org.uk   Lower Basildon, near Reading, Berkshire RG8 9NR
nationaltrust.org.uk/basildon-park

Bembridge Fort

Bembridge Down, near Bembridge, Isle of Wight PO36 8QY 1967

In a commanding position on Bembridge Down, this unrestored Victorian fort is part of the area's rich military history. **Note**: sorry no toilet. Not suitable for children under 10.

Find out more: 01983 741020 or bembridgefort@nationaltrust.org.uk c/o Longstone Farmhouse, Strawberry Lane, Mottistone, Isle of Wight PO30 4EA
nationaltrust.org.uk/bembridge-fort

Bembridge Windmill

Bembridge, Isle of Wight

1961 ☒ ⬆

The Isle of Wight's only surviving windmill is one of the island's most iconic buildings, built more than 300 years ago. The sails last turned in 1913, but inside most of its original machinery is still intact. Climb to the top and follow the milling process down four floors. **Note**: steep steps inside the windmill. **Satnav**: do not use, follow brown signs.

Access: ☒ ⬆

Find out more: 01983 873945 or bembridgemill@nationaltrust.org.uk High Street/Mill Road, Bembridge, Isle of Wight PO35 5SQ **nationaltrust.org.uk/bembridge-windmill**

Iconic Bembridge Windmill on the Isle of Wight

Compton Bay and Downs

Compton, Isle of Wight

1961 ⬆ ⬆

Compton Bay and Downs, Isle of Wight

With sandy beaches and colourful cliffs, Compton Bay is considered one of the best beaches on the island. It's also a prime site for fossil-hunting – look out for dinosaur foot casts. The clifftops and downs are rich in wildlife and easy-to-access walks, with views as far as Dorset. **Note**: steep steps down to the beach. **Satnav**: use PO30 4HB.

Find out more: 01983 741020 or comptonbay@nationaltrust.org.uk **nationaltrust.org.uk/compton-bay-and-downs**

Hinton Ampner

near Alresford, Hampshire

1986

Hinton Ampner is the fulfilment of one man's vision. After a catastrophic fire in 1960, Ralph Dutton rebuilt his home in the light and airy Georgian style he loved. A passionate collector, he filled the sunny rooms with ceramics and art. Outside, Dutton designed a series of tranquil garden rooms, each with their own distinctive planting still apparent today. Geometric topiary, exotic-coloured dahlias and borders of repeat-flowering roses lead onto terraces with panoramic views across the South Downs. Extensive lawns, a park with ancient oaks and beech woodland provide plenty of space to stroll, play, relax and picnic. **Satnav**: use SO24 0NH – takes you to Hinton Arms pub, 21 yards west of main entrance.

Access:

Find out more: 01962 771305 or hintonampner@nationaltrust.org.uk near Alresford, Hampshire SO24 0LA **nationaltrust.org.uk/hinton-ampner**

Hinton Ampner in Hampshire: the tranquil garden, above, and lovingly rebuilt house, below

Maidenhead and Cookham Commons

near Maidenhead, Berkshire

1934

This chain of ancient commons (below and bottom) offers footpaths through broadleaf woodlands, chalk downland, marshes dotted with orchids and hay meadows buzzing with insects in summer. These rich habitats are great for spotting wildlife throughout the year – you might see emperor dragonflies, marbled white butterflies, redwings, skylarks and fieldfares. **Satnav**: use SL6 9SB for Cookham Moor car park.

Find out more: 01628 605069 or maidenheadandcookham@nationaltrust.org.uk
nationaltrust.org.uk/maidenhead-and-cookham-commons

Mottisfont

near Romsey, Hampshire

1957

Mottisfont in Hampshire offers plenty of space for playing and discovery

Ancient trees, babbling brooks and rolling lawns frame this 18th-century house with a medieval priory at its heart. Maud Russell made Mottisfont her home in the 1930s, bringing artists here to relax and create works inspired by Mottisfont's past, including an extraordinary drawing room painted by Rex Whistler. We continue those artistic traditions today, with a permanent 20th-century art collection and major exhibitions in our top-floor gallery. Outside, carpets of spring bulbs, walled gardens, rich autumn leaves and a colourful winter garden create a feast for the senses all year. Our world-famous collection of old-fashioned roses flowers once a year in June. There are spaces to run, jump and play, and always something for families to do. **Satnav**: use SO51 0LN.

Access:

Find out more: 01794 340757 or mottisfont@nationaltrust.org.uk
near Romsey, Hampshire SO51 0LP
nationaltrust.org.uk/mottisfont

The magnificent rose garden at Mottisfont

Mottistone Gardens and Estate

Mottistone, near Brighstone,
Isle of Wight PO30 4ED

1965 ❀❤⚓

Set in a sheltered valley, these 20th-century gardens are filled with shrub-lined banks, hidden pathways and colourful borders. They surround an ancient manor house (not open) and have a Mediterranean-style planting scheme, taking advantage of the southerly location, including drought-tolerant plants and an olive grove. Other features include a monocot border, an organic kitchen garden and a tea garden alongside The Shack, a cabin retreat designed as their summer drawing office by architects John Seely (2nd Lord Mottistone) and Paul Paget. A network of footpaths crosses the adjoining Mottistone Estate, taking walkers high onto the downs via the historic Longstone.

Mottistone Gardens and Estate, Isle of Wight: the manor house, above, and gardens, below

Access: 🅿♿🅿♿

Find out more: 01983 741302 or mottistonegardens@nationaltrust.org.uk
nationaltrust.org.uk/mottistone-estate

The Needles Batteries and Headland

West High Down, Alum Bay,
Isle of Wight PO39 0JH

1975 🗾🏖🏛

Walking from Freshwater Bay to The Needles Headland along Tennyson Down, there are views as far as Dorset. At the end, high above The Needles, amid acres of countryside, is the Needles Old Battery. This Victorian fortification built in 1862 was used throughout both world wars. The Parade Ground has two original guns, and the military history is brought to life with displays, models and a series of vivid cartoons. An underground tunnel leads to

Perfect spot for a selfie at The Needles

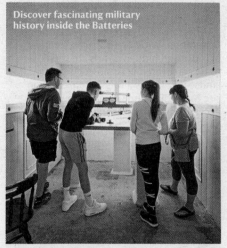

Discover fascinating military history inside the Batteries

The Needles and Headland, Isle of Wight

a searchlight emplacement with dramatic views over The Needles rocks at the tip of the island. The New Battery, further up the headland, was once a secret rocket-testing site used during the Cold War. **Note**: steep paths and uneven surfaces. Spiral staircase to tunnel. Toilet at Old Battery only.

Access: 🅿️♿🚻♿

Find out more: 01983 754772 or needles@nationaltrust.org.uk
nationaltrust.org.uk/the-needles-old-battery-and-new-battery

New Forest Commons and Foxbury

near East Wellow, Hampshire

1928

Woodland, grassland, heathland, bogs and mires make up the unique landscape of the New Forest Commons, a wilderness that's teeming with wildlife. The National Trust looks after commons at the following places: Bramshaw, Foxbury, Hale Purlieu, Hightown, as well as Rockford and Ibsley. Foxbury, a gateway to the New Forest, is a 150-hectare (370-acre) area of heathland restoration. Wide open spaces, gentle hillsides and hidden ponds are there to be discovered in this recovering landscape. This is a fragile conservation site for wildlife and we only allow access for special seasonal events.

New Forest Commons and Foxbury, Hampshire: a resident, top right, and visitor, below

Satnav: follow the Omega signs; for Foxbury use SO51 6AQ, Bramshaw Commons SO51 6AQ; Hale Purlieu SP6 2QZ; Hightown Common BH24 3HH; Rockford and Ibsley Commons BH24 3NA.

Find out more: 01425 650035 or newforest@nationaltrust.org.uk **nationaltrust.org.uk/new-forest-northern-commons**

Newtown National Nature Reserve and Old Town Hall

Newtown, near Shalfleet, Isle of Wight PO30 4PA

1933

On the water's edge, Newtown is home to a tranquil harbour, wildflower meadows and ancient woodland with rare butterflies and red squirrels. The only National Nature Reserve on the island, Newtown has been cared for by the National Trust since 1963.

Tucked away in a tiny hamlet adjoining the National Nature Reserve is the small and quirky 17th-century Old Town Hall, the only remaining evidence of Newtown's former importance. This historic building was the second to be bought and donated to the National Trust by Ferguson's Gang who were battling against the sprawling development of England in the 1930s. **Note**: nearest toilet in the car park by the visitor point.

Access: ♿ 🚾 ♨

Find out more: 01983 531622 (visitor point) or newtown@nationaltrust.org.uk
nationaltrust.org.uk/newtown-national-nature-reserve

Newtown National Nature Reserve and Old Town Hall, Isle of Wight: two views of the reserve

St Helens Duver

near St Helens, Isle of Wight

1928 ♨

Crisp, crunchy sand at St Helens Duver on the Isle of Wight

Once a Victorian golf course with royal patronage, St Helens Duver has sandy beaches, hidden rock pools, undulating sand dunes and coastal woods to explore. It's also a fascinating place to look for wildlife, from burrowing digger wasps to wasp spiders and waterbirds over the harbour. **Note**: sorry no toilet. **Satnav**: use PO33 1XY.

Find out more: 01983 741020 or sthelensduver@nationaltrust.org.uk
nationaltrust.org.uk/st-helens-duver

Sandham Memorial Chapel

Harts Lane, Burghclere, near Newbury,
Hampshire RG20 9JT

1947 ✝ ✿

Nestled in a quiet village, the Chapel hides
an unexpected treasure – an epic series of
paintings by the acclaimed artist Stanley
Spencer, depicting scenes inspired by his
experiences in the First World War. The
orchard is perfect for picnics and the
garden of reflection provides a peaceful
space for contemplation.

Access: P♿ D♿ ♿wc ⛽ ♿

Find out more: 01635 278394 or
sandham@nationaltrust.org.uk
nationaltrust.org.uk/sandham

**Sandham Memorial Chapel, Hampshire, contains
Stanley Spencer's epic First World War paintings**

The Vyne

Sherborne St John, near Basingstoke,
Hampshire

1956 🏠 ✝ ♿ ✿ 👥 👶

There is now more
than ever to see
at The Vyne,
Hampshire

The Vyne has opened more rooms than
ever before, including an exhibition space
revealing stories covering 500 years of
history. Visitors can discover the story of a
brother and sister who became intertwined
with The Vyne's survival: one the
unexpected heir to the grand Tudor
mansion; the other adopted as a
companion. Outside, acres of wildlife-rich
gardens and woods create a wonderful
space for relaxation and exploration, while
the play space gives children freedom to
let their imagination take them on an
adventure. Sweeping lawns offer lakeside
picnicking, and a short stroll reveals a bird
hide overlooking water meadows.

The Vyne's wildlife-rich gardens offer glorious colour and fascinating features

Satnav: not reliable, follow brown signs.

Access: [icons]

Find out more: 01256 883858 or
thevyne@nationaltrust.org.uk
Vyne Road, Sherborne St John, near
Basingstoke, Hampshire RG24 9HL
nationaltrust.org.uk/vyne

West Green House Garden

West Green, Hartley Wintney,
Hampshire RG27 8JB 1957

Four seasons of beauty, contrast and inspiration. Created by acclaimed garden designer and writer Marylyn Abbott. **Note**: maintained on behalf of the National Trust by Marylyn Abbott. Facilities not National Trust.

Find out more: 01252 844611 or
westgreenhouse@nationaltrust.org.uk
nationaltrust.org.uk/west-green-house-garden

Winchester City Mill

Bridge Street, Winchester, Hampshire

1929 [icons]

This restored working watermill has stood at the heart of the city of Winchester for a millennium and is probably the oldest working watermill in the UK. As the official Gateway to the South Downs National Park, City Mill is an insightful and integral part of any part of any visit to the South Downs. **Note**: nearest toilet 220 yards (not National Trust). **Satnav**: do not use.

Access: [icons]

Find out more: 01962 870057 or
winchestercitymill@nationaltrust.org.uk
Bridge Street, Winchester,
Hampshire SO23 9BH
nationaltrust.org.uk/winchester-city-mill

Winchester City Mill, Hampshire, may well be the oldest working watermill in the UK

Exploring the Walk Wood at
Sheffield Park and Garden,
East Sussex

Kent, Surrey and Sussex

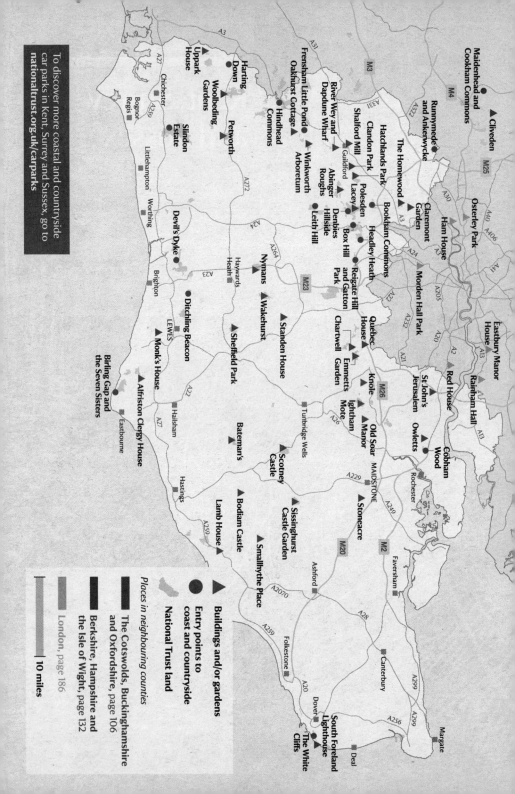

Abinger Roughs and Netley Park

White Downs Lane, Abinger Hammer, Surrey RH5 6QS 1940

Hidden woods, flower-filled grasslands, natural play and picnic benches make this the perfect spot for young nature explorers and families. **Note**: sorry no toilet.

Find out more: 01306 887485 (rangers) or abingerroughs@nationaltrust.org.uk
nationaltrust.org.uk/abinger-roughs-and-netley-park

Alfriston Clergy House

The Tye, Alfriston, Polegate, East Sussex BN26 5TL

1896

This rare 14th-century Wealden 'hall-house' (above) was the first building to be acquired by the National Trust, in 1896. The thatched, timber-framed house is in an idyllic setting, with views across the River Cuckmere, and is surrounded by a tranquil cottage garden full of wildlife. **Note**: nearest toilet in village car park.

Access: ⃞

Find out more: 01323 871961 or alfriston@nationaltrust.org.uk
nationaltrust.org.uk/alfriston

Bateman's

Bateman's Lane, Burwash, East Sussex TN19 7DS

1940

The tranquil lily pond at Bateman's, East Sussex, top, and inside the 17th-century house, above, which remains much as Rudyard Kipling left it

Bateman's remains today as Kipling described it in 1902: 'A grey stone lichened house – AD 1634 over the door – beamed, panelled, with oak staircase all untouched and unfaked… It is a good and peaceable place, standing in terraced lawns nigh to a walled garden of old red brick and two fat-headed old oast houses with red brick stomachs and an aged silver-grey dovecot [sic] on top.' Many of Kipling's belongings

Birling Gap and the Seven Sisters

near Eastbourne, East Sussex

1931

For drama, nothing beats the point where the sheer chalk cliffs of the South Downs meet the sea. One of the south coast's longest undeveloped stretches, the Seven Sisters are truly iconic. If you venture down the steps onto the beach,

The Seven Sisters provide a dramatic backdrop to the beach at Birling Gap, East Sussex

Kipling would recognise his desk at Bateman's, top, as so little has changed. The manicured lawns, above, are perfect for fun and games

remain as he left them. Paths wind past Kipling's 1928 Rolls-Royce, through manicured lawns and a wildflower meadow. A 17th-century working watermill stands beside the River Dudwell.

Access:

Find out more: 01435 882302 or batemans@nationaltrust.org.uk **nationaltrust.org.uk/batemans**

you can discover fascinating rock pools and the intricate wave-cut platform. The café and shop are a delightful place to start or end your peaceful downland walk. Before you explore the rare chalk heath and grassland, why not get some friendly advice from the visitor welcome team? **Note**: unstable cliff edge, stay away from edge and from cliff base. **Satnav**: use BN20 0AB.

Access:

Find out more: 01323 423197 or birlinggap@nationaltrust.org.uk
nationaltrust.org.uk/birling-gap

Bodiam Castle

Bodiam, near Robertsbridge, East Sussex TN32 5UA

 1926

A brooding symbol of power for more than 700 years, the strong stone walls of Bodiam Castle rise up proudly from the peaceful river valley setting. A wide moat encircles the seemingly untouched medieval exterior. Once inside, spiral stairways, tower rooms and battlements are ripe for exploration.

Bodiam Castle, East Sussex: brooding symbol of power for 700 years

Panoramic views across the Sussex countryside can be enjoyed from the top of the towers. Visitors of all ages are captivated by this evocative medieval ruin, a place where you can let your imagination run free. In spring and early summer Bodiam is home to a nationally significant bat maternity roost. **Note**: popular with schools. Main toilets in car park. Portaloos at top of site (main season).

Access: ⓟ ⓓ ⓦⓒ ⓐ ⓖ

Find out more: 01580 830196 or bodiamcastle@nationaltrust.org.uk
nationaltrust.org.uk/bodiam-castle

Let your imagination run free at
Bodiam Castle, above and below

Bookham Commons

near Great Bookham, Surrey

1923 ⚲

Bookham Commons, Surrey, is home to numerous butterflies and birds

Enchanting ancient oak woodland, grassland plains and tranquil ponds. Listen out for tuneful nightingales and warblers in the spring and in summer look for insects hovering over the ponds. If you're lucky, you may also spot the beautiful, but elusive, purple emperor butterfly.
Note: sorry no toilet.
Satnav: use KT23 3LT.

Access: ⓐ

Find out more: 01306 887485 or bookhamcommons@nationaltrust.org.uk
nationaltrust.org.uk/bookham-commons

Box Hill

Tadworth, Surrey

1914

A great place for family adventures: delving into the ancient woodland, exploring the natural play trail, finding the tower or discovering the River Mole at the Stepping Stones. On a clear day you can see for miles from the top of Box Hill, so if you're hiking up along one of the many footpaths, the stunning views are well worth it. Box Hill and Westhumble and Dorking railway stations are within easy reach. **Satnav**: use KT20 7LB (doesn't work for all satnavs).

Access:

Find out more: 01306 888793 or boxhill@nationaltrust.org.uk
nationaltrust.org.uk/box-hill

You can see for miles from Box Hill in Surrey, above, or simply spend the day walking, below

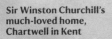

Sir Winston Churchill's much-loved home, Chartwell in Kent

Download the app to get opening details on your phone – scan the QR code on page 3

Chartwell

Mapleton Road, Westerham, Kent TN16 1PS

1946 🏠❁♿

Chartwell: Sir Winston Churchill's home

Chartwell was the family home of Sir Winston Churchill, the place that brought him comfort and inspiration. Filled with treasures and personal belongings from every aspect of his life, this intimate house invites you into the private world of one of Britain's greatest leaders. Follow in the footsteps of one of the many frequent guests who are recorded in the visitor book. His studio contains the largest collection of Churchill's paintings and offers an insight into Churchill the painter. The garden reflects Churchill's love of landscape and nature, including the lakes he created. There are lots of fun things to do in our woodland area: a tree house, Donkey Jack's caravan, swings, a bomb crater and much more to explore. **Note**: steep slopes; challenging for less able.

Access: 🅿️🅿️🔼🎵♿

Find out more: 01732 868381 or chartwell@nationaltrust.org.uk
nationaltrust.org.uk/chartwell

Clandon Park

near Guildford, Surrey

1956 🏠❁

A major project is under way at Clandon Park, to remake this Palladian mansion following the large fire in 2015. The house and garden will offer different types of access throughout the year, providing a unique opportunity to follow the Trust's progress as Clandon is re-imagined. **Satnav**: follow brown signs to the entrance on the A247.

Access: 🅿️🔼

Find out more: 01483 222482 or clandonpark@nationaltrust.org.uk West Clandon, near Guildford, Surrey GU4 7RQ
nationaltrust.org.uk/clandon-park

Come and see how Clandon Park in Surrey is being re-imagined after its devastating fire, bottom and below

The lake at Claremont Landscape Garden in Surrey

Claremont Landscape Garden

near Esher, Surrey

1949 ✤

One of the earliest 18th-century landscape gardens, Claremont was once described as 'the noblest of any in Europe', combining the innovative work of designers Vanbrugh, Bridgeman, Kent and 'Capability' Brown. Once a playground for the wealthy and influential, and a sanctuary for British, French and Belgian royalty, retrace the steps of Queen Victoria, Princess Charlotte and Prince Leopold. The impressive turf

Dressing-up fun at Claremont Landscape Garden

amphitheatre offers wonderful views over the lake, and walks take in features such as the grotto and camellia terrace. Explore our play area for younger children or Badger's Basecamp, a den-building area for older children. **Satnav**: unreliable; instead follow brown signs from Cobham and Esher.

Access: 🅿♿ 🖼♿ ♿

Find out more: 01372 467806 or claremont@nationaltrust.org.uk Portsmouth Road, near Esher, Surrey KT10 9JG **nationaltrust.org.uk/claremont-landscape-garden**

Cobham Wood and Mausoleum

near Cobham, Kent 2014

Sitting proud in historic woodland pasture, the 18th-century Darnley Mausoleum commands stunning views across the North Kent downs. **Note**: access to mausoleum on foot only, about 1 mile from South Lodge Barn. **Satnav**: use DA12 3BS.

Find out more: 01732 810378 or cobham@nationaltrust.org.uk **nationaltrust.org.uk/cobham**

Denbies Hillside

near Dorking, Surrey

1963

Denbies Hillside is a dramatic chalk escarpment with panoramic views of the Surrey countryside. It's a great place to walk, picnic and watch wildlife – you may even spot chalk downland species such as the Adonis blue and chalkhill blue butterflies. **Satnav**: use RH5 6SR.

Access:

Find out more: 01306 887485 or denbieshillside@nationaltrust.org.uk
nationaltrust.org.uk/denbies-hillside

Panoramic view from Denbies Hillside in Surrey

Devil's Dyke

near Brighton, West Sussex

1995

Dyke Valley at Devil's Dyke in West Sussex

Cycling challenge at Devil's Dyke

At nearly a mile long, the Dyke Valley is the longest, deepest and widest 'dry valley' in the UK. Legend has it that the Devil dug this chasm to drown the parishioners of the Weald. On the other hand, scientists believe it was formed naturally just over 10,000 years ago in the last ice age. The walls of

Ditchling Beacon

near Ditchling, East Sussex

1953

Just 7 miles north of Brighton, at 248 metres above sea level, Ditchling Beacon is the highest point in East Sussex and offers panoramic views all around the summit. To the south visitors can see the sea, while to the north you look across the Weald or east–west across the Downs. The site also has the remains of an Iron Age hill fort. Situated on the South Downs Way, it makes an excellent place to start a walk heading west towards Devil's Dyke or east towards Black Cap and Lewes.

Crisp white snow at Ditchling Beacon in East Sussex

Wintry landscape at Devil's Dyke, top, and delicate fungi, above

the Iron Age hill fort can be seen when you walk around the hill, and there is a carpet of flowers and a myriad of colourful insects to discover in the valley. **Satnav:** use BN1 8YJ.

Access:

Find out more: 01273 857712 or devilsdyke@nationaltrust.org.uk
nationaltrust.org.uk/devils-dyke

Cattle grazing at Ditchling Beacon

Satnav: use BN6 8XG.

Access: [Pᵢ]

Find out more: 01323 423197 or
ditchlingbeacon@nationaltrust.org.uk
nationaltrust.org.uk/ditchling-beacon

Emmetts Garden

Ide Hill, Sevenoaks, Kent TN14 6BA

[1965] ✦ ♨

**Vivid spring colour at Emmetts Garden in Kent:
a stunning Edwardian horticultural gem**

Emmetts is a rare, stunning Edwardian
garden known for its beautiful bluebells and
spring colour. Summer brings the romantic
rose garden, followed by vibrant autumn
foliage, and more than 1,000 winter bulbs
newly planted – there is something to see
all year, as well as wonderful views across
the Weald of Kent that can be enjoyed from
the garden and on our countryside walks.
Emmetts is a garden to enjoy with friends
and family, a place where you can let off
steam, play games, picnic in our meadow
or simply sit back and relax.

Note: a five-year restoration scheme is under way in some areas of the garden.

Access: [icons]

Find out more: 01732 868381 or emmetts@nationaltrust.org.uk
nationaltrust.org.uk/emmetts

Emmetts Garden, below and bottom, offers new delights every season. There are also countryside walks to enjoy

Frensham Little Pond

Priory Lane, Frensham, Surrey GU10 3BT

1974 [icon]

Originally created in the 11th century to supply the Bishop of Winchester with fish, the pond and surrounding area is now a sanctuary for wildlife. The heathland is a colourful mosaic of purple heathers, fragrant bright-yellow gorse and rich green bracken with many footpaths to explore. **Note**: to protect the wildlife habitats, swimming and inflatables are not allowed.

Access: [icon]

Find out more: 01428 681050 (rangers) or frenshamlittlepond@nationaltrust.org.uk
nationaltrust.org.uk/frensham-little-pond

Harting Down

near South Harting, West Sussex 1994

A tapestry of downland with scattered scrub and woodland, rich in wildlife and steeped in history. **Note**: nearest toilets at South Harting or Uppark.
Satnav: unreliable.

Find out more: 01730 816638 or hartingdown@nationaltrust.org.uk
nationaltrust.org.uk/harting-down

Hatchlands Park

East Clandon, Guildford, Surrey GU4 7RT

1945

With open fields grazed by sheep and cattle, ancient woodland and wildflower meadows, the parkland is perfect for relaxation and exploration. The natural adventure area, with its tree house and bug burrow, is perfect for families to get even closer to nature. Nestled in the parkland is a Georgian country house, built for naval hero Admiral Boscawen and his wife, Fanny.

Exploring the parkland at Hatchlands Park in Surrey, top, and inside the opulent house, below

Now home to tenant Alec Cobbe, it contains his collection of Old Master paintings and the Cobbe Collection – Europe's largest array of keyboard instruments, including some which inspired world-famous composers such as J S Bach and Elgar. **Note**: only six ground-floor rooms open. **Satnav**: follow brown signs to main car park entrance on A246.

Access:

Find out more: 01483 222482 or hatchlands@nationaltrust.org.uk
nationaltrust.org.uk/hatchlands

Headley Heath

Headley Common Road, Headley Heath, Surrey KT18 6NN 1946

A wide network of tracks to explore, featuring a wonderful mosaic of heath, chalk downland and mixed woodland. **Note**: cattle grazing. Car parks at Headley Heath and Brimmer.

Find out more: 01306 885502 or headleyheath@nationaltrust.org.uk
nationaltrust.org.uk/headley-heath

Hindhead Commons and the Devil's Punch Bowl

near Hindhead, Surrey

1906

Spectacular views from Hindhead Commons and uninterrupted walks to the Devil's Punch Bowl make this an unforgettable place to relax and take in some of the best countryside in the South East. Since the opening of the A3 tunnel, paths and bridleways have been reconnected and natural contours restored. Peace and calm now reign and the glorious landscape, with its carpets of purple heather in the summer and grazing Highland cattle, is there to enjoy.

Glorious Hindhead Commons and the Devil's Punch Bowl in Surrey

Highland cattle graze Hindhead Commons and the Devil's Punch Bowl

Satnav: use GU26 6AB.

Access:

Find out more: 01428 681050 (rangers) or hindhead@nationaltrust.org.uk
nationaltrust.org.uk/hindhead-and-devils-punchbowl

The Homewood

Portsmouth Road, Esher, Surrey KT10 9JL
1999

Patrick Gwynne's extraordinary early 20th-century family home is a masterpiece of Modernist design in the midst of a picturesque garden. **Note**: administered on behalf of the National Trust by tenant. Nearest toilets and café at Claremont.

Find out more: 01372 467806 (Claremont Landscape Garden) or thehomewood@nationaltrust.org.uk c/o Claremont Landscape Garden, Portsmouth Road, Esher, Surrey KT10 9JG
nationaltrust.org.uk/homewood

Ightham Mote

Mote Road, Ivy Hatch, near Sevenoaks, Kent TN15 0NU

1985 [icons]

Hidden away in a secluded Kent valley – a location it owes to the wealth of natural resources and proximity to water – this perfectly preserved medieval moated manor house is just over 700 years old. Ightham Mote's architecture and decoration reflect the development of the English country house, while its past owners provide the many stories about this once-cherished family home, evoking a deep sense of history. In the tranquil gardens there are streams and lakes fed by natural springs, an orchard, flower borders and a cutting garden. The wider estate offers walks with secret glades and countryside views.

Fiery autumn colours light up woodland on Ightham Mote's estate

Note: very steep slope from visitor reception – passenger buggy or lower drop-off available. **Satnav**: use TN15 0NU.

Access: [icons]

Find out more: 01732 810378 or ighthammote@nationaltrust.org.uk Mote Road, Ivy Hatch, near Sevenoaks, Kent TN15 0NT **nationaltrust.org.uk/ightham-mote**

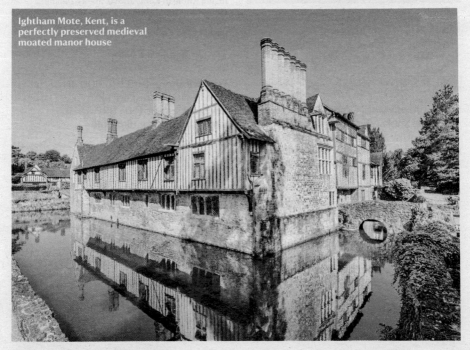

Ightham Mote, Kent, is a perfectly preserved medieval moated manor house

Knole

Sevenoaks, Kent

1946

Sitting proudly within Kent's last medieval deer park, Knole offers a vast estate where you can follow in the footsteps of tourists who have visited Knole's show rooms for 400 years. The recently conserved rooms showcase one of the finest collections of Royal Stuart furniture and textiles, and feature paintings by renowned artists. Spend the day and take in panoramic views from the top of the Gatehouse Tower, where you can also discover the life and loves of a former resident. See the scale and magnificence of this 600-year-old estate by exploring the grand courtyards or wandering through the parkland.
Satnav: use TN13 1HX and follow brown signs to Sevenoaks High Street (entrance opposite St Nicholas Church).

Inside Knole in Kent, above, are astonishing collections and fabulous rooms to discover. While outside, below, there is beautiful parkland to explore

Access:

Find out more: 01732 462100 or
knole@nationaltrust.org.uk
Sevenoaks, Kent TN15 0RP
nationaltrust.org.uk/knole

Lamb House

West Street, Rye, East Sussex TN31 7ES

1950

Georgian Lamb House in East Sussex: home to both Henry James and E. F. Benson

Georgian home of writers Henry James and E. F. Benson, who depicted the property in the *Mapp and Lucia* stories. There is a peaceful walled garden, full of colour, designed by Alfred Parsons, as well as a vegetable patch – unusual in the heart of Rye. **Note**: restricted access for buggies and wheelchairs.

Find out more: 01797 222909 or lambhouse@nationaltrust.org.uk
nationaltrust.org.uk/lamb-house

Leith Hill

near Coldharbour, Dorking, Surrey

1923

Leith Hill Tower is the highest point in south-east England, offering unbeatable views north to London and south to see the sea sparkling through Shoreham Gap. The house, Leith Hill Place, was gifted by composer Ralph Vaughan Williams, and used for a time as a school boarding house. Now it is a venue for exhibitions and workshops. You can enjoy walks on the hill, where every season is a riot of colour – starting with the spring bluebells at Frank's Wood, followed by the early summer colour at the Rhododendron Wood and then the stunning autumnal displays of golds and reds.

Leith Hill, Surrey: views for miles and miles

Leith Hill Place, this picture, and dramatic Leith Hill Tower, above

Monk's House

near Lewes, East Sussex

1980 🏠 ✿

Monk's House in East Sussex, the simple country retreat of Virginia Woolf

This small 16th-century weatherboarded cottage in the village of Rodmell was the country retreat of novelist Virginia Woolf and her husband Leonard and a meeting place for the Bloomsbury Group. The garden features the room where she created her best-known works and includes cottage garden borders, orchard, allotments and ponds.
Note: no access to Rodmell from A26.
Satnav: do not use – wrongly indicates access over railway crossing.

Note: sorry no toilet; steep spiral stairs to top. **Satnav**: for Rhododendron Wood and Starveall Corner use RH5 6LU (height restriction barrier); for Windy Gap RH5 6LX; for Landslip RH5 6HG.

Access: ♿

Access: 🅿♿

Find out more: 01306 712711 (Leith Hill Tower). 01306 711685 (Leith Hill Place) or leithhill@nationaltrust.org.uk
nationaltrust.org.uk/leith-hill

Find out more: 01273 474760 or monkshouse@nationaltrust.org.uk
Rodmell, near Lewes, East Sussex BN7 3HF
nationaltrust.org.uk/monks-house

Nymans

Handcross, near Haywards Heath,
West Sussex RH17 6EB

1954 🏛️ 🌸 🧩

A garden for all seasons, with rare and
unusual plant collections, set around a
romantic house and partial ruins. The
comfortable, yet elegant, house reflects
the personalities and stories of the talented
Messel family. In spring see blossom,
bulbs and a stunning collection of subtly
fragranced magnolias. The Rose Garden,
inspired by Maud Messel's 1920s design,
is scented by hints of old-fashioned roses.
Dramatic shows of vibrant native tree
colour in autumn precede winter's

**Romantic Nymans in West Sussex: the elegant
house, below, is surrounded by a garden for all
seasons, above, filled with rare and unusual plants**

Two views, above, of the exceptional garden at Nymans, which is bursting with colour and scent

Oakhurst Cottage

Hambledon, near Godalming,
Surrey GU8 4HF 1952

Timber-framed cottage offering a rare insight into domestic life in the mid-19th century, with a traditional garden to explore. **Note**: nearest toilets and visitor facilities at Winkworth Arboretum.

Find out more: 01483 208936 (Winkworth Arboretum) or oakhurstcottage@nationaltrust.org.uk
nationaltrust.org.uk/oakhurst-cottage

Old Soar Manor

Plaxtol, Borough Green,
Kent TN15 0QX 1947

Dating from 1290, the remaining rooms of this knight's house offer a glimpse back to the time of Edward I. **Note**: sorry no toilet. Narrow lanes.

Find out more: 01732 810378 or oldsoarmanor@nationaltrust.org.uk
nationaltrust.org.uk/old-soar-manor

structural form, with pockets of perfumed daphne throughout the garden. Discover hidden corners through stone archways, walk along tree-lined avenues while surrounded by the lush countryside of the Sussex Weald. The adjoining woodland, with lake and bird hides, has plenty of opportunities to spot wildlife.

Access: ♿ ♿ ♿ ♿ ♿ ♿

Find out more: 01444 405250 or nymans@nationaltrust.org.uk
nationaltrust.org.uk/nymans

Owletts

The Street, Cobham, Gravesend,
Kent DA12 3AP 1938

An architect's 17th-century family home with a varied history and architectural features, set within a relaxing, traditional garden.

Find out more: 01732 810378 or owletts@nationaltrust.org.uk
nationaltrust.org.uk/owletts

Petworth

Petworth, West Sussex

1947

Inspired by the Baroque palaces of Europe, Petworth House is an extraordinary and surprising ancestral seat created by one family over 900 years. The 17th-century building you see today comprises grand state rooms which form the centrepiece of your visit. Designed to display the taste, lifestyle and artistic patronage of generations, the state rooms offer an infinity of paintings and sculpture, including major works by Van Dyck, Turner, Reynolds and Gainsborough. This remarkable

Extraordinary Petworth in West Sussex, above and below, was inspired by European Baroque palaces

collection reflects a family's journey of survival and success through the Tudor Reformation, Gunpowder Plot and the Napoleonic Wars. **Note**: selected rooms may be closed over the winter for conservation. **Satnav**: use GU28 9LR.

Access: [icons]

Find out more: 01798 342207 or petworth@nationaltrust.org.uk Petworth, West Sussex GU28 0AE **nationaltrust.org.uk/petworth**

Petworth's grand interiors, such as the Staircase Hall, bottom, are matched by equally splendid grounds, below

Polesden Lacey

near Dorking, Surrey

1942 [icons]

Fun in the garden of Polesden Lacey, Surrey

Set within the Surrey Hills Area of Outstanding Natural Beauty, this was the party house of indomitable socialite Margaret Greville. Discover the many stories of Margaret's life, her lavish parties and domestic staff within this 19th-century house. There is also an astonishing collection, including pieces by Fabergé, maiolica and paintings by Dutch Masters. Surrounded by 12 hectares (30 acres) of grounds and a 566-hectare (1,400-acre) estate, there's space to walk and explore. The gardens offer colour and fragrance all year. Highlights include the walled rose garden in summer and the picturesque Graham Stuart Thomas-designed winter garden. Enjoy a woodland walk on the wider estate, home to wildlife, including rare birds and butterflies. The breathtaking views change with every season. **Satnav**: use KT23 4PZ.

Access: [icons]

Find out more: 01372 452048 or polesdenlacey@nationaltrust.org.uk Great Bookham, near Dorking, Surrey RH5 6BD **nationaltrust.org.uk/polesden-lacey**

There is so much
space to walk and
explore in Polesden
Lacey's garden,
grounds and estate

Quebec House

Quebec Square, Westerham, Kent TN16 1TD

1918

Quebec House, Kent, was the childhood home of General James Wolfe

The childhood home of General James Wolfe, Quebec House retains much of its original charm and feel. Recreated Georgian schoolroom, hands-on collections and objects belonging to Wolfe are used to learn about Georgian family life. Exhibition in the Coach House explores Wolfe's victory at the Battle of Quebec in 1759.

Access:

Find out more: 01732 868381 or quebechouse@nationaltrust.org.uk
nationaltrust.org.uk/quebec-house

Reigate Hill and Gatton Park

near Reigate, Surrey

1912

Reigate Hill commands sweeping views across the Weald to the South Downs. It's a great spot for walking, family picnics, flying a kite and watching wildlife. A short walk away is the 19th-century Reigate Fort. The complex is open every day and the fort buildings open for special events. To the east of Reigate Hill is Surrey Hill's hidden gem, Gatton Park, designed by Lancelot 'Capability' Brown.

Reigate Hill and Gatton Park in Surrey, top right and below: so many perfect picnic spots

Note: areas of Gatton Park opened monthly by the Gatton Trust. **Satnav**: use RH2 0HX.

Access: 🚶

Find out more: 01342 843036 or reigate@nationaltrust.org.uk **nationaltrust.org.uk/reigate-hill-and-gatton-park**

River Wey and Godalming Navigations and Dapdune Wharf

Navigations Office and Dapdune Wharf, Wharf Road, Guildford, Surrey GU1 4RR

1964 🏠♿

A hidden haven where you can relax and unwind on a boat trip, explore a restored barge, or enjoy scenic walks. Dapdune Wharf in Guildford brings to life stories of the historic waterway, along 20 miles of waterside towpath. A great place for children to have fun. **Note**: boat trip charges, mooring and fishing fees apply to members.

Access: ♿🚻

Find out more: 01483 561389 or riverwey@nationaltrust.org.uk **nationaltrust.org.uk/river-wey-and-godalming-navigations-and-dapdune-wharf**

Taking to the water on the River Wey, Surrey

Runnymede and Ankerwycke

Egham, near Old Windsor, Surrey

1931 🏠🚲♿🚶

Seen by many as the birthplace of modern democracy, this picturesque landscape beside the Thames was witness to King John's sealing of the Magna Carta more than 800 years ago. Within easy reach of the M25, there is so much to enjoy here – ancient woodlands, countryside walks and picnics by the river. Along with Lutyens's Fairhaven Lodges, Runnymede is home to memorials for the Magna Carta, John F. Kennedy and Commonwealth Air Forces, making it the perfect place to reflect.

Runnymede and Ankerwycke in Surrey, this picture and right: so much history, and so much to enjoy

Note: mooring and fishing (during fishing season) available for additional fee (including members). **Satnav**: use TW20 0AE and follow brown 'Runnymede Memorials' signs.

Access: ♿🚻♿

Find out more: 01784 432891 or runnymede@nationaltrust.org.uk
nationaltrust.org.uk/runnymede

St John's Jerusalem

Sutton-at-Hone, Dartford, Kent DA4 9HQ
1943

Set within a secluded moated garden, this is a rare example of a 13th-century chapel built by the Knights Hospitaller. **Note**: private residence, maintained and managed by a tenant on behalf of the National Trust. Sorry no tea-room or accessible toilet.

Find out more: 01732 810378 or stjohnsjerusalem@nationaltrust.org.uk
nationaltrust.org.uk/st-johns-jerusalem

Scotney Castle, Kent: the romantic ruins of the moated old castle

Scotney Castle

Lamberhurst, Tunbridge Wells,
Kent TN3 8JN

1970 🏠🏚️🛁❄️🎎

The medieval moated Old Scotney Castle lies in a peaceful wooded valley. In the 19th century its owner, Edward Hussey III, set about building a new house, partially demolishing the Old Castle to create a romantic folly, the centrepiece of his picturesque landscape. From the terraces

The new house at Scotney Castle is a homely and characterful Victorian mansion

of the new house, sweeps of rhododendrons and azaleas cascade down the slope in summer, followed by highlights of autumn leaf colour, mirrored in the moat. In the house three generations have made their mark, adding possessions and character to the homely Victorian mansion which enjoys far-reaching views out across the estate.

Access: 🅿️🅿️♿🚹♿

Find out more: 01892 893820 (Infoline). 01892 893868 or scotneycastle@nationaltrust.org.uk
nationaltrust.org.uk/scotney-castle

Shalford Mill

Shalford, near Guildford,
Surrey GU4 8BS 1932

Evocative mill, although the machinery no longer works. Discover the story of the Ferguson's Gang. **Note**: sorry no toilet or refreshments.

Find out more: 01483 561389 or shalfordmill@nationaltrust.org.uk
nationaltrust.org.uk/shalford-mill

Sheffield Park and Garden

Sheffield Park, Uckfield,
East Sussex TN22 3QX

1954 ♣ 🏊

Originating in the 18th century and developed by each subsequent owner, this garden of colour, perfume and sound excites your senses as you enjoy winding paths, majestic trees, ponds and dappled glades. Falls, cascades and bridges are integral to the garden design. Planting is reflected in ponds so clear that the eye is tricked into thinking up is down. Bold and grand planting has a sculptural form in winter. Spring and summer bring vibrant blooms, fragrant arbours and splashes of colour. Autumn is a blazing kaleidoscope of greens, flame-reds, burnt oranges and bright yellows, planted for their combined display. The encircling park and woodland provide opportunities for further adventure where nature thrives in riverside meadows and woods. **Satnav:** look out for brown signs on approach.

Access: 🅿️ 🅳 ♿ 📶 ♿ 🚻

Find out more: 01825 790231 or sheffieldpark@nationaltrust.org.uk
nationaltrust.org.uk/sheffield-park-and-garden

Sheffield Park and Garden, East Sussex, this page and opposite, offers bold planting as well as grand design

Sissinghurst Castle Garden

Biddenden Road, near Cranbrook,
Kent TN17 2AB

1967

Sissinghurst Castle Garden sits within the ruin of a great Elizabethan house surrounded by the rich Kentish landscape of woods, streams and farmland. The famous garden, with its fairy-tale tower, is the result of the creativity of the formal design of Harold Nicolson and the lavish planting of Vita Sackville-West. The colour schemes, intimacy of the different garden 'rooms' and rich herbaceous borders are the epitome of an English garden.

Sissinghurst Castle Garden in Kent offers so many photo opportunities

Slindon Estate

near Arundel, West Sussex

1950

Slindon Estate is a patchwork of woodland, downland, farmland and parkland, with an unspoilt Sussex village at its centre. Historic features cover the landscape, such as Stane Street, the Roman road from Chichester to London. Slindon has a rich and wonderfully varied wildlife with bats, badgers, butterflies and downland flowers.

A froth of cow parsley on Slindon Estate in West Sussex

An exquisite border at Sissinghurst Castle Garden, above, and the distinctive turreted gatehouse, top

The wider estate, which includes a vegetable garden, lakes and rich variety of wildlife, is waiting to be explored, while our regular exhibitions tell Sissinghurst's stories and show how history and landscape have combined to shape this special place. See the architectural beauty of the garden in winter at weekends. **Note**: limited access for buggies and wheelchairs.

Access:

Find out more: 01580 710700 or sissinghurst@nationaltrust.org.uk
nationaltrust.org.uk/sissinghurst

Note: sorry no toilet. **Satnav**: use BN18 0QY for Park Lane; BN18 0SP Duke's Road; RH20 1PH Bignor Hill.

Find out more: 01243 814730 or slindonestate@nationaltrust.org.uk
nationaltrust.org.uk/slindon-estate

Smallhythe Place

Smallhythe, Tenterden, Kent TN30 7NG

1939

Surrounded by the rolling Kent countryside, the corridors of this early 16th-century cottage resonate with the vibrant spirit of its theatrical former owner, Victorian actress Ellen Terry. Bursting with memorabilia from her life-long career on stage, visitors can see unique theatrical artefacts and visit the Barn Theatre.

Access:

Find out more: 01580 762334 or smallhytheplace@nationaltrust.org.uk
nationaltrust.org.uk/smallhythe-place

Ellen Terry's vibrant spirit is evident everywhere at Smallhythe Place in Kent

South Foreland Lighthouse

The Front, St Margaret's Bay, Dover, Kent

1989

South Foreland Lighthouse in Kent: historic landmark

This historic landmark, dramatically situated on The White Cliffs of Dover, guided ships past the infamous Goodwin Sands and has a fascinating tale to tell. It was the first lighthouse powered by electricity and the site of the first international radio transmission. **Note:** access to lighthouse by road is not permitted.

Access:

Find out more: 01304 853281 or southforeland@nationaltrust.org.uk
Langdon Cliffs, Dover, Kent CT16 1HJ
nationaltrust.org.uk/south-foreland-lighthouse

Standen House and Garden in West Sussex: outstanding Arts and Crafts rural retreat in an idyllic location

Standen House and Garden

West Hoathly Road, East Grinstead, West Sussex RH19 4NE

1973 🏛️ ✿ ⚘

James and Margaret Beale chose an idyllic location to build their rural retreat, nestled in the Sussex countryside with views across the High Weald. Designed by Philip Webb, the house is one of the finest examples of Arts and Crafts workmanship with Morris & Co. interiors and decorative art of the period. The 5-hectare (12-acre) hillside

Standen House has fine Morris & Co. interiors

garden established by Mrs Beale is restored to its 1920s glory. Each garden room offers something for every season, from colourful spring bulbs to autumn shades. On the wider estate, footpaths lead into the woodlands and the High Weald Area of Outstanding Natural Beauty.

Access: 🅿️ 🔵 ♿ ♨️ ♿

Find out more: 01342 323029 or standen@nationaltrust.org.uk
nationaltrust.org.uk/standen-house-and-garden

Stoneacre

Otham, Maidstone, Kent ME15 8RS 1928

Medieval farmhouse sitting within a hidden horticultural haven, orchard, meadows and woodland. Home to famous designer and critic Aymer Vallance.

Find out more: 01580 710701 or stoneacre@nationaltrust.org.uk
nationaltrust.org.uk/stoneacre

Uppark House and Garden

South Harting, Petersfield,
West Sussex GU31 5QR

1954 ⚑ ✿

High on its vantage point on the South Downs ridge, Uppark has views as far south as the Solent. Outside, the intimate garden is being gradually restored to its historical design, with plenty of space in the adjacent meadow to play and relax. Filled with purchases from the Grand Tour, Uppark's Georgian interiors illustrate the comfort of life 'upstairs' in contrast to the 'downstairs' world of its servants. Highlights include one of the best examples of an 18th-century British doll's house in the country.

Uppark House and Garden in West Sussex, above and below, sits high up on the South Downs

Note: due to conservation work, access to some areas may be limited.

Access: 🅿️ 🅳 🖼️ 📷 ♿

Find out more: 01730 825415 or uppark@nationaltrust.org.uk
nationaltrust.org.uk/uppark

Wakehurst

Ardingly, Haywards Heath,
West Sussex RH17 6TN

1964 🏠❀⚒️📷

Wakehurst, Kew's wild botanic garden in Sussex, has more than 202 hectares (500 acres) of beautiful ornamental gardens, woodlands and a nature reserve. Internationally significant for collections, scientific research and plant conservation, you can also visit Kew's unique Millennium Seed Bank, where science and horticulture work side by side. **Note**: funded and managed by the Royal Botanic Gardens, Kew. **Parking charges apply (including members).**

Access: 🅿️ ♿ ♿ ♿

Find out more: 01444 894066 or
wakehurst@kew.org
**nationaltrust.org.uk/wakehurst
kew.org**

Wakehurst, West Sussex: Kew's wild botanic garden has collections which are significant worldwide

The White Cliffs of Dover

Langdon Cliffs, Dover, Kent

1968 🏠⚒️🏛️

The White Cliffs of Dover in Kent have been a symbol of hope for generations

There can be no doubt that The White Cliffs of Dover are one of this country's most spectacular natural features and have been a symbol of hope for generations. You can appreciate their beauty through the seasons by taking one of the country's most dramatic clifftop walks, which offer unrivalled views of the English Channel while savouring the rare flora and fauna found only on this chalk grassland.

Winkworth Arboretum

Hascombe Road, Godalming,
Surrey GU8 4AD

1952 ✿ ▥

The National Trust's only arboretum was
born from one man's vision and passion.
Dr Wilfrid Fox used the wooded valley and
its lakes as a canvas for 'painting a picture'
with trees. The fruits of his labour are an
award-winning collection of more than

Winkworth Arboretum in Surrey
boasts more than 1,000 varieties of
trees and shrubs

**The White Cliffs of Dover:
entering Fan Bay Deep Shelter,
top, and a clifftop walk, above**

Fan Bay Deep Shelter, a labyrinth of
forgotten Second World War tunnels, is a
reminder of the fascinating military history
of The White Cliffs. **Note**: nearest toilets at
White Cliffs. Age restrictions apply at Fan
Bay. **Satnav**: use CT15 5NA.

Access: ᴘ♿ ⓦⒸ ♿ ♿

Find out more: 01304 202756 or
whitecliffs@nationaltrust.org.uk
nationaltrust.org.uk/white-cliffs

1,000 varieties of trees and shrubs set in the picturesque Surrey Hills, offering stunning combinations of colour every season. Famous for vibrant autumnal foliage and carpets of bluebells in spring, the azaleas, magnolias and snowdrops make Winkworth worth visiting all year round for beautiful scenery, picnics and events for all ages. **Note**: some steep slopes; banks of lake and wetlands only partially fenced.

Access: 🅿️♿📶

Find out more: 01483 208477 or winkwortharboretum@nationaltrust.org.uk
nationaltrust.org.uk/winkworth

Woolbeding Gardens

Midhurst, West Sussex GU29 9RR

1957 ✤

Woolbeding Gardens in West Sussex is an ever-changing horticultural haven

Bordering the River Rother, Woolbeding Gardens is a horticultural haven where modern yet romantic planting meets sophisticated colour palettes. Elegant garden rooms and meticulous borders merge with a wooded landscape that conceals dramatic architectural follies. Ever-changing, from the seasons to the planting, every moment offers something new and picturesque. **Note**: access by park-and-ride minibus from Midhurst.

Access: 🅿️♿📶♿

Find out more: 0344 249 1895 or woolbedinggardens@nationaltrust.org.uk
nationaltrust.org.uk/woolbeding-gardens

London

Relaxing in the Stables Walled Garden at Osterley Park and House in Isleworth

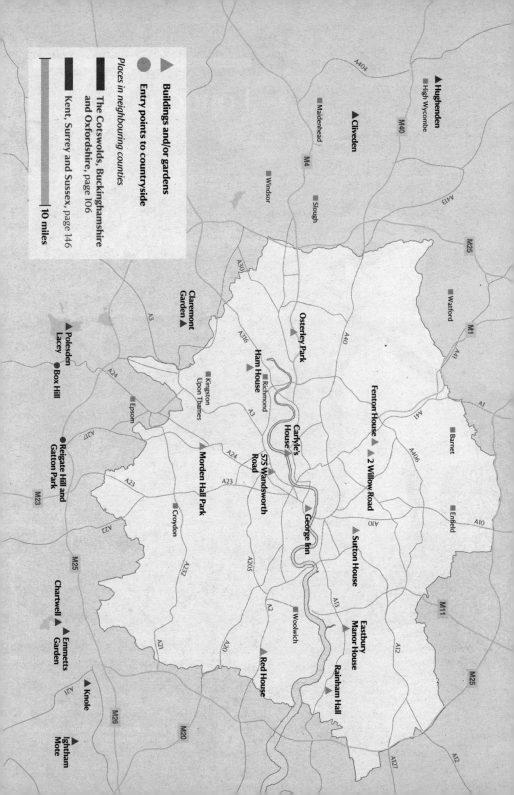

Places in neighbouring counties

The Cotswolds, Buckinghamshire and Oxfordshire, page 106

Kent, Surrey and Sussex, page 146

Buildings and/or gardens

Entry points to countryside

10 miles

▲ Hughenden
■ High Wycombe

A404

M40

▲ Cliveden

■ Maidenhead

M4

■ Windsor

■ Slough

A413

M25

■ Watford

M1

A41

Claremont Garden ▲

A3

A30

▲ Polesden Lacey
● Box Hill

A24

■ Epsom

A316

Osterley Park ▲

Ham House ▲
■ Richmond

■ Kingston Upon Thames

A3

A40

Fenton House ▲

Carlyle's House ▲

2 Willow Road ▲

Sutton House ▲

A41

A406

■ Barnet

A1

■ Enfield

A10

M11

M25

▲ Morden Hall Park

A24

575 Wandsworth Road ▲

A23

George Inn ▲

A205

A2

Eastbury Manor House ▲

A13

Rainham Hall ▲

A12

A127

M25

A23

■ Croydon

A232

A22

M23

● Reigate Hill and Gatton Park

A217

■ Woolwich

A20

A21

Red House ▲

A2

M25

Chartwell ▲

Emmetts Garden ▲

M26

A21

▲ Knole

M20

▲ Ightham Mote

A21

Carlyle's House

24 Cheyne Row, Chelsea, London SW3 5HL

1936 ⬛⬛

Hidden in the quiet back streets of Chelsea, the home of Victorian writer Thomas Carlyle and his amusing wife Jane, was visited by their many friends, including such literary giants as John Ruskin, Charles Dickens and William Makepeace Thackeray. Small walled garden.

Access: ⬛

Find out more: 020 7352 7087 or carlyleshouse@nationaltrust.org.uk
nationaltrust.org.uk/carlyles-house

The elegant hallway of Carlyle's House in Chelsea

Eastbury Manor House

Eastbury Square, Barking IG11 9SN

1918 ⬛⬛

Dressing up, above, at Elizabethan Eastbury Manor House in Barking, top

Barely altered since it was built circa 1573, this Grade I-listed Elizabethan gentry house features soaring chimneys, early 17th-century wall-paintings and an original turret staircase. Outside there is a cobbled courtyard and peaceful walled garden with bee boles to explore. **Note**: managed by London Borough of Barking and Dagenham. Some rooms are closed occasionally for functions.

Access: ⬛⬛⬛⬛

Find out more: 020 8227 2942 or eastburymanor@nationaltrust.org.uk
nationaltrust.org.uk/eastbury-manor-house

Fenton House and Garden

Hampstead Grove, Hampstead, London NW3 6SP

 1952

This 1686 house (above), with views across London from Hampstead's Holly Hill, is filled with world-class collections of ceramics, paintings, textiles and musical instruments. The ever-changing horticultural gem that is the garden includes an orchard, kitchen garden, rose garden, terraces and lawns, and never fails to delight.

Access:

Find out more: 020 7435 3471 or fentonhouse@nationaltrust.org.uk
nationaltrust.org.uk/fenton-house

George Inn

The George Inn Yard, 77 Borough High Street, Southwark, London SE1 1NH 1937

This public house, dating from the 17th century, is London's last remaining galleried inn. **Note:** leased to a private company.

Find out more: 020 7407 2056 or georgeinn@nationaltrust.org.uk
nationaltrust.org.uk/george-inn

Ham House and Garden

Ham Street, Ham, Richmond TW10 7RS

1948

Beautifully situated on the banks of the River Thames, Ham is truly one of London's treasures. You can step back in time, walking on the original marble floors while admiring the lavish furnishings, cabinets and artwork collected by the Duke and Duchess of Lauderdale and enjoyed by Charles II during his visits here. The re-imagining of the 17th-century garden

is quite wonderful. Containing a large walled kitchen garden, lavender parterre, woodland wilderness garden, two wildflower meadows and boasting an annual display of spring bulbs, the garden's creation was designed to impress. **Satnav**: takes you to stables on nearby Ham Street, carry straight on past these to car park.

Access:

Find out more: 020 8940 1950 or hamhouse@nationaltrust.org.uk
nationaltrust.org.uk/ham-house

Step back in time at Ham House and Garden in Richmond, below and right: truly one of London's treasures

Ornate footbridge
at South London's
Morden Hall Park

Morden Hall Park

Morden Hall Road, Morden,
London SM4 5JD

 1941

A duckling enjoys the river at Morden Hall Park

Step into this 50-hectare (125-acre) oasis and you'll soon forget you're in bustling South London. Once a private country estate, the grounds were gifted to the National Trust to become a park for all people, and have been a local treasure ever since. Peaceful tree-lined riverside paths lead to wide open meadows and a collection of historic buildings which hint at an industrial past. The 1920s rose garden is a delight for the senses in summer and a perfect picnic spot, while a stroll on the immersive wetland boardwalk gives a rare glimpse into the secretive world of waterbirds.

Access:

Find out more: 020 8545 6850 or
mordenhallpark@nationaltrust.org.uk
nationaltrust.org.uk/morden-hall-park

Osterley Park and House

Isleworth, London

1949

A suburban palace caught between town and country, Osterley Park and House is one of the last surviving country estates in London. Past fields and grazing cattle, just around the lake the magnificent house awaits, presented as it would have been when it was redesigned by Robert Adam in the late 18th century for the Child family. A place for welcoming friends and clients, fashioned for show and entertaining, the lavish state apartments tell the story of a party palace. Recently returned family

Osterley Park and House in Isleworth, below and bottom, is one of the last surviving country estates in London

Download the app to get opening details on your phone – scan the QR code on page 3

portraits and furniture now add a personal touch to grand rooms. Elegant pleasure gardens and hundreds of acres of parkland are perfect for whiling away a peaceful afternoon. **Satnav**: enter Jersey Road and TW7 4RD.

Access:

Find out more: 020 8232 5050 or osterley@nationaltrust.org.uk
Jersey Road, Isleworth, London TW7 4RB
nationaltrust.org.uk/osterley-park

Family fun in the kitchen garden, left, and the lavish Entrance Hall at Osterley, below

Rainham Hall

The Broadway, Rainham, London RM13 9YN

1949

Lying at the very heart of Rainham village, Rainham Hall is a hidden piece of London history

Built in 1729 for an enterprising merchant, Rainham Hall lies at the heart of Rainham village on the far-eastern fringe of London. Surrounded by wild marshland and thriving industry, this hidden piece of London's history has been home to nearly 50 different inhabitants, including a scientist-vicar and a *Vogue* photographer.

Access:

Find out more: 01708 525579 or rainhamhall@nationaltrust.org.uk
nationaltrust.org.uk/rainham

Red House

Bexleyheath, London

2003 🏛️✣

The only house commissioned, created and lived in by William Morris, founder of the Arts and Crafts movement, Red House (above) is a building of extraordinary architectural and social significance. An ongoing conservation project is gradually revealing Red House's secrets, including original pre-Raphaelite wall-paintings and Morris's first decorative schemes. **Satnav:** use DA6 8HL – Danson Park car park.

Access: 🅿️♿📳

Find out more: 020 8303 6359 or redhouse@nationaltrust.org.uk
Red House Lane, Bexleyheath, London DA6 8JF
nationaltrust.org.uk/red-house

Sutton House and Breaker's Yard

2 and 4 Homerton High Street, Hackney, London E9 6JQ

1938 🏛️✣

For nearly 500 years Sutton House has reflected and adapted to the world around it; its identity ranging from a country house to an East London squat. Today it continues to reflect Hackney, hosting hundreds of visits from community and school groups, as well as events and weddings all year.

Access: 🅿️♿📳♿

Find out more: 020 8986 2264 or suttonhouse@nationaltrust.org.uk
nationaltrust.org.uk/sutton-house

Sutton House and Breaker's Yard in Hackney, below and bottom, hosts hundreds of visits and events

575 Wandsworth Road

575 Wandsworth Road, Lambeth,
London SW8 3JD

2010 ♿

Khadambi Asalache (1935–2006) turned
this modest Grade II-listed Georgian
terraced house (above) into a work of art.
Featuring hand-carved fretwork throughout,
the house and collections continue to
inspire all who visit. Please wear or bring
socks as no outdoor shoes are allowed in
the house. **Note**: sorry no toilet or café.

Find out more: 0344 249 1895 (bookings)
or 575wandsworthroad@nationaltrust.org.uk
**nationaltrust.org.uk/575-wandsworth-
road**

2 Willow Road

Hampstead, London NW3 1TH

1994 ♿

This late 1930s house (below), an architect's
vision of the future, paints a vivid picture
of the creative and social circles in which
Ernö and Ursula Goldfinger moved. Today
you can explore the intimate and evocative
interiors, innovative designs, intriguing
personal possessions and impressive
20th-century art collection.
Note: sorry no toilet.

Access: 🅿️ 🅿️ ♿

Find out more: 020 7435 6166 or
2willowroad@nationaltrust.org.uk
nationaltrust.org.uk/2-willow-road

East of England

Discovering the opulent
West Drawing Room at
Oxburgh Hall in Norfolk

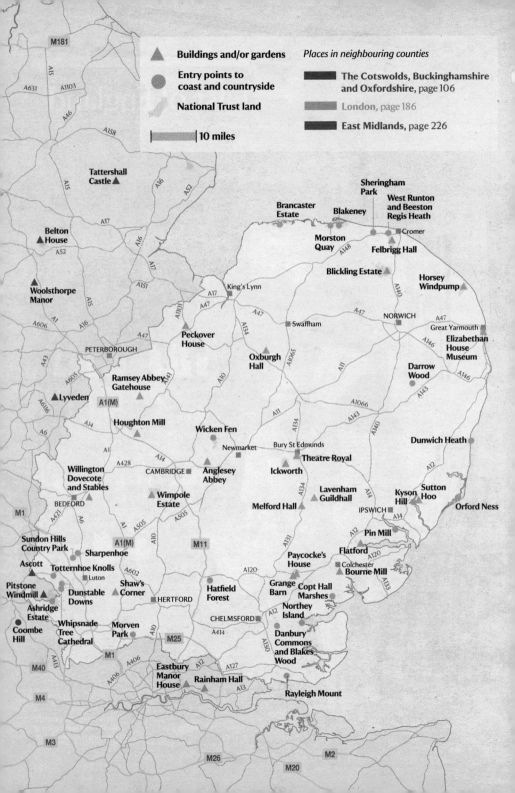

Buildings and/or gardens

Entry points to coast and countryside

National Trust land

Places in neighbouring counties

The Cotswolds, Buckinghamshire and Oxfordshire, page 106

London, page 186

East Midlands, page 226

10 miles

M181

A15
A631
A1103
A46
A158
A16
A52

Tattershall Castle ▲

Belton ▲ House
A52
A16
A17
A151
A101

Woolsthorpe Manor
A15
A1
A606
A16
A43
A605
A6116

▲Lyveden
A1(M)

PETERBOROUGH
A47

Peckover House
A134
A10

Ramsey Abbey Gatehouse
A47

Houghton Mill
A14
A1

King's Lynn
A17
A47
A47

Swaffham

NORWICH

Oxburgh Hall
A1065
A11

Wicken Fen
Newmarket
A14

Willington Dovecote and Stables
A428
A14
CAMBRIDGE
A1

Wimpole Estate
A505

BEDFORD
A1(M)
A505
A10
M11

Sundon Hills Country Park
Sharpenhoe

Ascott
Totternhoe Knolls
Luton
A602

Pitstone Windmill ▲
Dunstable Downs
Shaw's Corner
HERTFORD

Ashridge Estate

Coombe Hill

Whipsnade Tree Cathedral
Morven Park
A10
M25

M40
M1
A406
A406
A13

Eastbury Manor House
Rainham Hall
A12
A127

M4

M3

M26
M20
M2

Brancaster Estate
Morston Quay
A148
Blakeney
Sheringham Park
West Runton and Beeston Regis Heath
Cromer

Felbrigg Hall
Blickling Estate
A140

Horsey Windpump ▲

A47
Great Yarmouth
A146
Elizabethan House Museum
A146
A143

Darrow Wood

A1066
A143
A140

Dunwich Heath
A12

Theatre Royal
Bury St Edmunds

Ickworth
A134

Lavenham Guildhall
A14

Kyson Hill
Sutton Hoo

Melford Hall
IPSWICH
A14

Orford Ness

A12
Pin Mill
Flatford
A120

Paycocke's House
A131

Copt Hall Marshes
Grange Barn
A120

Colchester
Bourne Mill
A133

Hatfield Forest

Northey Island
A12
CHELMSFORD
A414
A130

Danbury Commons and Blakes Wood

Rayleigh Mount

Anglesey Abbey, Gardens and Lode Mill, Cambridgeshire: the welcoming house, above, and gardens, below

Anglesey Abbey, Gardens and Lode Mill

Quy Road, Lode, Cambridge, Cambridgeshire CB25 9EJ

1966 🏠 🏛 ✿

This welcoming and elegant house, gardens and working watermill have something to offer in every season. The nationally celebrated 50-hectare (124-acre) gardens, with sweeping avenues, wildflower meadows, classical statuary and flower borders, offer reflective space, captivating views, vibrant colours and delicious scents throughout the year. Families can play, explore and discover nature in the wider woodland. The house showcases Lord

The fascinating library at Anglesey Abbey

Historic watermill on beautiful Quy Water

Fairhaven's extensive and unique collection, including seasonal highlights bringing its story to life, and one of the most significant 20th-century libraries in the National Trust. The historic watermill, on beautiful Quy Water, provides a unique insight into a critical part of East Anglian life.

Access: 🅿🚻♿♿♿

Find out more: 01223 810080 or
angleseyabbey@nationaltrust.org.uk
nationaltrust.org.uk/angleseyabbey

Ashridge Estate

near Berkhamsted, Hertfordshire

1926 ✖🏛🐾

This special place has been enjoyed for centuries by everyone from pilgrims to picnickers. With its rich wildlife, diverse habitats and varied history, there is plenty to uncover at Ashridge. From the scent of the bluebells in spring, glorious birdsong and spectacular views from the chalk downland of the Ivinghoe Hills in summer,

the rutting fallow deer in autumn and crisp walks on swathes of open common in winter, Ashridge has a landscape for every season. Waymarked trails available from the visitor centre. Wildwood Den natural play area for children. Climb the Bridgewater Monument for fantastic views. **Note**: toilets available only when café open. **Satnav**: use HP4 1LT for the visitor centre and Bridgewater Monument.

Access: 🅿️♿🚻📷♿♿

Find out more: 01442 851227 or ashridge@nationaltrust.org.uk
nationaltrust.org.uk/ashridge

For centuries everyone from pilgrims to picnickers have enjoyed Ashridge Estate in Hertfordshire

Blakeney National Nature Reserve

near Morston, Norfolk

 1912 🏠🏛️♿📷👥

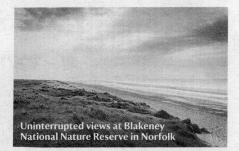

Uninterrupted views at Blakeney National Nature Reserve in Norfolk

At the heart of the Norfolk Coast Area of Outstanding Natural Beauty, internationally important Blakeney National Nature Reserve boasts wide open spaces and uninterrupted views. Blakeney Point, a 4-mile shingle spit, is home to a vast array of resident and migratory wildlife, including summer-breeding terns and winter-breeding grey seals. **Note**: nearest toilets at Morston Quay and Blakeney Quay (not National Trust). **Satnav**: use NR25 7BH for Morston Quay or NR25 7NE for Blakeney Quay.

Access: ♿📷

Find out more: 01263 740241 or blakeneypoint@nationaltrust.org.uk
nationaltrust.org.uk/blakeney

One of the wide open spaces at Blakeney

Blickling Estate in Norfolk: the sheer beauty of the Jacobean mansion will take your breath away

Blickling Estate

Blickling, Aylsham, Norfolk NR11 6NF

1940

Blickling's walled garden produces fruit, vegetables and herbs in abundance

You'll never forget your first sight of Blickling, as the breathtaking Jacobean mansion comes into view, flanked by ancient yew hedging and encircled by its historic park. This 1,933-hectare (4,700-acre) gift to the nation was bequeathed by its visionary owner, Lord Lothian, whose role was pivotal in creating the 1937 Act of Parliament that allowed whole estates to be left to the National Trust without incurring death duties. Your support is helping to tackle some of the crucial conservation work needed to protect the most significant library held by the National Trust and the Long Gallery that houses it.

Access:

Find out more: 01263 738030 or blickling@nationaltrust.org.uk
nationaltrust.org.uk/blickling

Bourne Mill

Bourne Road, Colchester, Essex CO2 8RT

1936

Built for banquets and converted into a mill in the 17th century, Bourne Mill still has a working waterwheel. The surrounding pond, wetlands and woods are home to a variety of wildlife, including birds, bats, waterfowl and many insects, which provide endless nature discoveries.

Access:

Find out more: 01206 549799 or bournemill@nationaltrust.org.uk
nationaltrust.org.uk/bourne-mill

Bourne Mill in Essex, below, was originally built for banquets. Its surrounding pond, bottom, is home to a huge variety of wildlife

Brancaster Estate

near Brancaster, Norfolk

1923

Beautiful Brancaster Beach on the Brancaster Estate, Norfolk

The Brancaster Estate comprises the beautiful endless sandy Brancaster Beach, perfect for summer sandcastles and winter walks, the intriguing Branodunum Roman Fort site and the traditional fishing harbour of Brancaster Staithe. The area is rich in wildlife and offers a memorable visit regardless of the time of year. **Note**: beach car park (not National Trust). Toilets at beach and harbour. **Satnav**: use PE31 8AX (Beach Road); PE31 8BW (Brancaster Staithe).

Access: 🖺

Find out more: 01263 740241 or brancaster@nationaltrust.org.uk
nationaltrust.org.uk/brancaster-estate

Copt Hall Marshes

near Little Wigborough, Essex 1989

Working farm on the remote and beautiful Blackwater Estuary – important for overwintering species. **Note**: sorry no toilet. St Nicholas Church not National Trust. **Satnav**: use CO5 7RD.

Find out more: copthall@nationaltrust.org.uk
nationaltrust.org.uk/copt-hall-marshes

Danbury Commons and Blakes Wood

near Danbury, Essex 1953

Varied countryside, ranging from the lowland heath of Danbury Commons to ancient woodland at Blakes Wood. **Note**: sorry no toilet. **Satnav**: for Danbury Commons use CM3 4JH; for Blakes Wood use CM3 4AU.

Find out more: 01245 227662 or danbury@nationaltrust.org.uk
nationaltrust.org.uk/danbury-commons-and-blakes-wood

Darrow Wood

near Harleston, Norfolk 1990

Small, hedge-enclosed, lightly wooded pasture field containing earthworks, including remains of a compact motte-and-bailey castle. **Note**: sorry no toilet. **Satnav**: use IP20 0AY, Darrow Green Road.

Find out more: 01728 648020 (Dunwich Heath) or darrowwood@nationaltrust.org.uk
nationaltrust.org.uk/darrow-wood

Dunstable Downs and the Whipsnade Estate

near Dunstable, Bedfordshire

Plenty of space for fun on Dunstable Downs

1928 🏛️🏊🐾

The Downs have so much to offer all year round. As well as being the best kite-flying and picnicking site for miles around, Dunstable Downs are a haven for plants and wildlife, including orchids, butterflies, birds and much more. Enjoy the ever-changing view from the Chilterns Gateway Centre with a refreshing drink or delicious meal.

Note: Chilterns Gateway Centre is owned by Central Bedfordshire Council and managed by the National Trust.
Satnav: use LU6 2GY.

Access: 🅿️🚻♿🚪♿

Find out more: 01582 500920 or dunstabledowns@nationaltrust.org.uk
nationaltrust.org.uk/dunstable

Dunstable Downs and the Whipsnade Estate in Bedfordshire

Dunwich Heath and Beach, Suffolk

Dunwich Heath and Beach

near Saxmundham, Suffolk

1968 🏖️🚶🐾

Dunwich Heath has been in the care of the National Trust for more than 50 years. A precious landscape on the Suffolk coast, Dunwich Heath offers a true sense of being at one with nature. Located in the middle of an Area of Outstanding Natural Beauty, there is an abundance of wildlife, including

Trying to spot some of the abundant wildlife at Dunwich Heath and Beach

rare birds such as the Dartford warbler and the mysterious nightjar, as well as herds of red deer. The network of footpaths allows you to immerse yourself in nature and explore different habitats, including heather heath, gorse tracks, open grassland, woodland, shingle beach and sandy cliffs. **Satnav**: use IP17 3DJ.

Access: 🅿️♿️🚻♿️♿️

Find out more: 01728 648501 or dunwichheath@nationaltrust.org.uk
nationaltrust.org.uk/dunwich-heath

Elizabethan House Museum

4 South Quay, Great Yarmouth, Norfolk NR30 2QH 1943

A 16th-century quayside home, set out to reflect day-to-day domestic life from Tudor to Victorian times. **Note**: managed by Norfolk Museums Service.

Find out more: 01493 855746 or elizabethanhouse@nationaltrust.org.uk
nationaltrust.org.uk/elizabethan-house-museum

Felbrigg Hall, Gardens and Estate

Felbrigg, near Cromer, Norfolk

1969 🏛️✝️❄️♿

Atmospheric Felbrigg is a place of tranquillity. The Hall, which still contains its original and extensive collection, reflects the people who shaped it. A home to many generations, it has more than 400 years of family stories to be discovered. Set in extensive parkland, with a working walled garden and dove-house, orangery, lake, ancient woodland and miles of estate walks, all framed by big Norfolk skies, Felbrigg is the perfect place to escape and relax at any time of year. **Satnav**: use NR11 8PP.

Access: 🅿️ 🅳 ♿ ♿ ♿

Find out more: 01263 837444 or felbrigg@nationaltrust.org.uk
Felbrigg, near Cromer, Norfolk NR11 8PR
nationaltrust.org.uk/felbrigg

Felbrigg Hall, Gardens and Estate, Norfolk: the tranquil Hall, above and below, contains a fascinating collection

Inspirational and charming
Flatford in Suffolk

Flatford

East Bergholt, Suffolk CO7 6UL

1943

Access: 📍 ♿ 🚻 ♿ ♿ ♿

Find out more: 01206 298260 or
flatford@nationaltrust.org.uk
nationaltrust.org.uk/flatford

Splashing in the shallows of the River Stour

Flatford lies at the heart of the Dedham Vale Area of Outstanding Natural Beauty. This charming hamlet was the inspiration for some of John Constable's most famous paintings, including *The Hay Wain*, *Boat Building* and *Flatford Mill*. The fascinating exhibition gives you an insight into Constable's life and career while Bridge Cottage tells the story of the people who lived and worked at Flatford. You can explore the beautiful countryside on one of the circular walks or follow riverside paths to the nearby villages of Dedham and East Bergholt. A visit to Flatford is a chance to walk in Constable's footsteps. **Note**: no public access inside Flatford Mill, Valley Farm and Willy Lott's House.

Grange Barn

Grange Hill, Coggeshall, Colchester,
Essex CO6 1RE

1989 🏠

One of Europe's oldest timber-framed
buildings, Grange Barn stands as a lasting
reminder of the once-powerful Coggeshall
Abbey. With oak pillars soaring up to a
cathedral-like roof, bearing the weight of
centuries, it was saved and restored in the
1980s. This 13th-century building has truly
stood the test of time.

Access: 🅿️ ♿

Find out more: 01376 562226 or
grangebarn1@nationaltrust.org.uk
nationaltrust.org.uk/grange-barn

Grange Barn in Essex is one of Europe's
oldest timber-framed buildings

Hatfield Forest National Nature Reserve

near Bishop's Stortford, Essex

1924 🏠🏛️🔍♿🚶

Hatfield Forest National Nature Reserve in Essex

When Henry I established a royal hunting
forest here in 1100, he could little have
guessed that almost a millennium later it
would be the best survivor of its kind in
the world. The forest is now an important
National Nature Reserve and has been
recognised as a Site of Special Scientific
Interest since the 1950s, due to its breadth
of habitats and wildlife. Explore the wide
open plains, grazed by Red Poll cattle, or
enjoy the shade of the coppice woodland.

Horsey Windpump

Horsey, Great Yarmouth, Norfolk NR29 4EE

1948 ✕♨⛩✿

Restored and standing proud over the Broadland landscape, Horsey Windpump is complete with winding cap and patent sails. Explore this historic building and discover its fascinating story and the connection between man and nature. There are fantastic views over Horsey Mere and beyond from the top.
Note: surrounded by Horsey Estate – managed by the Buxton family.

Access: ♿🚻♿

Find out more: 01263 740241 or horseywindpump@nationaltrust.org.uk
nationaltrust.org.uk/horsey

With its new sails and winding cap, Horsey Windpump rises proudly above the flat Norfolk Broads

Locals at Hatfield Forest, top, and visitors, above

With more than 405 hectares (1,000 acres), there are many places for imaginative play or quiet relaxation. **Note**: to protect the forest, the best time to visit is May to September. **Satnav**: use CM22 6NE.

Access: ♿🚻♿♿

Find out more: 01279 870678 or hatfieldforest@nationaltrust.org.uk
nationaltrust.org.uk/hatfield-forest

Houghton Mill and Waterclose Meadows

Houghton, near Huntingdon,
Cambridgeshire PE28 2AZ

1939

Historic watermill in an inspiring riverside setting surrounded by meadow walks. All the family can enjoy exploring the oldest working watermill on the Great Ouse. You can buy flour, ground in the traditional way on our French burr millstones.

Access:

Find out more: 01480 499990 (mill). 01480 499996 (campsite) or houghtonmill@nationaltrust.org.uk
nationaltrust.org.uk/houghton-mill-and-waterclose-meadows

Ickworth

The Rotunda, Horringer, Bury St Edmunds, Suffolk IP29 5QE

1956

An Italianate palace in the heart of an ancient deer park. Formal gardens, pleasure grounds, rolling Suffolk landscape and woodlands invite gentle strolls, long walks, runs, bike rides and picnics. The Italianate Garden mirrors the architecture of the house and celebrates the Hervey family's passion for Italy, while also encasing an idiosyncratic Victorian stumpery. The Rotunda is home to one of the finest silver collections in Europe, family portraits by Gainsborough and Reynolds, works by Titian and Velázquez, and Neo-classical sculpture. The servants' quarters recreate domestic service through the stories and memories of those who lived here.

The Italianate rotunda at Ickworth in Suffolk

Ickworth's gardens, pleasure grounds and woodlands are perfect for a wet, splashy walk

Satnav: may not direct you to main entrance. Access to Ickworth is through Horringer village.

Access: ⬚⬚⬚⬚⬚⬚

Find out more: 01284 735270 or ickworth@nationaltrust.org.uk
nationaltrust.org.uk/ickworth

Kyson Hill

Broomheath, Woodbridge, Suffolk 1934

Kyson Hill, with its grassy slopes, specimen trees and views, is a small, but favourite destination for walking and relaxation.
Note: sorry no toilet. Broomheath public car park, 546 yards (not National Trust).
Satnav: For satnav use IP12 4DL.

Find out more: 01394 389700 (Sutton Hoo) or kysonhill@nationaltrust.org.uk
nationaltrust.org.uk/kyson-hill

Lavenham Guildhall

Market Place, Lavenham, Sudbury, Suffolk CO10 9QZ

1951 ⬚ ⬚

The Guildhall of Corpus Christi is a remarkable testament to the last 500 years of village life. This complex of timber-framed buildings provides an atmospheric backdrop to the stories of the people who shaped and influenced its fortunes and, ultimately, the village of Lavenham we see today. Sometimes sad, sometimes uplifting, their tales are poignant and life-affirming. From religious guild to workhouse, family home to nightclub, there is more than meets the eye. Take the opportunity to

There is more to Lavenham Guildhall in Suffolk, this picture and top, than first meets the eye

explore Lavenham village, known for its beautiful timber-framed buildings and impressive church.

Access: 🅳♿🚻

Find out more: 01787 247646 or lavenhamguildhall@nationaltrust.org.uk
nationaltrust.org.uk/lavenham-guildhall

Melford Hall

Long Melford, Sudbury, Suffolk CO10 9AA

1960 🏠❀🚶

Despite facing ransacking and fire, Melford Hall, Suffolk, survives as a much-loved family home

Melford Hall is a family home that has suffered its fair share of trials and tribulations, from being ransacked during the Civil War to being devastated by fire in 1942. It is thanks to the many generations who have called it home and left their mark, that it continues to survive. It is their stories, and those of the Hyde Parker family who currently live there – ranging from naval exploits to visits from their cousin Beatrix Potter – that make this family home such an intriguing place to explore.

Morston Quay

Quay Lane, Holt, Norfolk NR25 7BH

1973

A quiet corner of Morston Quay in Norfolk

Set just within the shelter of Blakeney Point, which forms a wonderful backdrop, tranquil Morston Quay is the perfect spot from which to explore this beautiful coastline. Hop onto a boat and go to see the seals on Blakeney Point, or simply sit and watch the world go by.

Access:

Find out more: 01263 740241 or morstonquay@nationaltrust.org.uk

Morven Park

near Potters Bar, Hertfordshire 1928

The site of the original Toll Bar, these 8 hectares (20 acres) of parkland were created 150 years ago. **Note**: sorry no toilet. **Satnav**: use EN6 1HS.

Find out more: 01582 873663 or morvenpark@nationaltrust.org.uk
nationaltrust.org.uk/morven-park

Melford Hall's elegant interiors, above, and fabulous garden, top, make for a rewarding visit

Access:

Find out more: 01787 376395 (Infoline). 01787 379228 or melford@nationaltrust.org.uk
nationaltrust.org.uk/melford-hall

Northey Island

near Maldon, Essex [1978]

A peaceful retreat on the Blackwater Estuary, important for overwintering birds, Northey is also the oldest recorded battlefield in Britain. **Note**: access by tidal causeway. **Satnav**: use CM9 6PP (CM9 5JQ for parking).

Find out more:
northeyisland@nationaltrust.org.uk
nationaltrust.org.uk/northey-island

Orford Ness National Nature Reserve

Orford Quay, Orford, Woodbridge, Suffolk IP12 2NU

[1993] 🏠♿🎨🐾

Suffolk's secret coast – wild, remote, exposed. Known as the 'Island', only reached by National Trust ferry, the Ness (below) contains the ruined remnants of a disturbing past. Ranked among the most important shingle features in the world, rare and fragile wildlife thrives where weapons, including atomic bombs, were tested and perfected.

Note: steep, slippery steps, long distances. Hazardous debris.

Access: 🅿️♿

Find out more: 01394 450900 or orfordness@nationaltrust.org.uk
nationaltrust.org.uk/orford

Oxburgh Hall

Oxborough, near Swaffham, Norfolk PE33 9PS

[1952] 🏠✝❀♿

Oxburgh Hall in Norfolk reveals a story of endurance

Built 500 years ago by the still-resident Bedingfeld family, Oxburgh has endured turbulent times. In 2019 we embarked on an ambitious project to restore the roof, dormers and chimneys, ensuring the fabric of the building for years to come. You can

Paycocke's House and Garden

25 West Street, Coggeshall, Colchester, Essex CO6 1NS

1924 🏛️ ✣

Set in an ancient village full of listed buildings, this exquisitely carved half-timbered Tudor cloth merchant's house offers five centuries of craftsmanship and conservation. Explore the many architectural changes and see how the house was saved from demolition and restored to its former glory, then discover the tranquil cottage garden.

Access: 🅳🅹 ♿ ♿

Find out more: 01376 561305 or paycockes@nationaltrust.org.uk **nationaltrust.org.uk/paycockes-house-and-garden**

There are five centuries of craftsmanship to admire at Paycocke's House and Garden in Essex

Oxburgh Hall is full of treasured objects, top, while outside there are a wildlife-rich garden, above, woods and parkland to explore

still explore parts of the house filled with portraits and treasured objects and the story of the conservation work. Outside you can catch reflections in the moat, relax in the wildlife-rich seasonal garden, and explore the acres of woodland, streams and parkland.

Access: 🅿️ ♿ ♿ ♿

Find out more: 01366 328258 or oxburghhall@nationaltrust.org.uk **nationaltrust.org.uk/oxburgh**

Peckover House and Garden in Cambridgeshire is an oasis of calm

Peckover House and Garden

near Wisbech, Cambridgeshire

1943 🏛️🏵️

While its riverside setting at Wisbech was popular among merchants, imposing Peckover House stood apart as an oasis of calm, reflecting the Quaker way of life. The Peckovers were bankers and added a specially designed wing to the house; an exhibition tells its story. The family also loved their garden, and you can discover its delights as you explore the unexpected 0.8 hectare (2 acres) of abundance. **Satnav**: use PE13 1RG or PE13 2RA for nearest car parks.

Access: 🅿️🖼️🚻🪑♿🚌

Find out more: 01945 583463 or peckover@nationaltrust.org.uk   North Brink, near Wisbech, Cambridgeshire PE13 1JR
nationaltrust.org.uk/peckover

Pin Mill

near Chelmondiston, Suffolk 1978

A woodland and heathland restoration site. A number of footpaths from the village with panoramic views over the River Orwell. **Satnav**: use IP9 1JW.

Find out more: pinmill@nationaltrust.org.uk
nationaltrust.org.uk/pin-mill

Ramsey Abbey Gatehouse

Hollow Lane, Ramsey, Huntingdon, Cambridgeshire PE26 1DH 1952

This fascinating medieval gatehouse, along with the Lady Chapel, are all that remain of the great Benedictine abbey at Ramsey. **Note**: on school grounds so no public access except on open days.

Find out more: 01480 499992 or ramseyabbey@nationaltrust.org.uk
nationaltrust.org.uk/ramsey-abbey-gatehouse

Rayleigh Mount

Rayleigh, Essex 1923

Medieval motte-and-bailey castle site, with adjacent windmill housing historical exhibition. **Satnav**: use SS6 7ED.

Find out more: 01284 747500 or rayleighmount@nationaltrust.org.uk
nationaltrust.org.uk/rayleigh-mount

Sharpenhoe

near Streatley, Bedfordshire 1939

Managed as a nature reserve; archaeology, geology and nature come together to provide a stunning landscape. **Note**: sorry no toilet. **Satnav**: use LU3 3PR.

Find out more: 01582 873663 or sharpenhoe@nationaltrust.org.uk
nationaltrust.org.uk/sharpenhoe

Shaw's Corner

Ayot St Lawrence, near Welwyn, Hertfordshire AL6 9BX

1944

George Bernard Shaw's peaceful, rural Arts and Crafts-inspired home and garden show what inspired this great playwright and social activist. Pictures and sculpture reflect his wide circle of influential friends and interests. **Note**: access roads are very narrow. **Satnav**: some routes might take you through a ford and an unsignposted route.

Access:

Find out more: 01438 821968 (Infoline). 01438 820307 or shawscorner@nationaltrust.org.uk
nationaltrust.org.uk/shaws-corner

The perfect writing spot at Shaw's Corner, Hertfordshire: Bernard Shaw's writing hut

Looking towards the distant North Norfolk coast at Sheringham Park, Norfolk

Sheringham Park

Upper Sheringham, Norfolk NR26 8TL

1987

Making use of the park's undulating landscape, Humphry Repton created views of the North Norfolk coast that can still be enjoyed today. His 1812 design stated 'Sheringham Park had more natural beauty and advantages than any place he had ever seen'. The Upcher family added an extensive rhododendron collection to Repton's design, bringing an array of colour to the wild garden in the spring.

With its wide array of birdlife, Sheringham Park is the perfect place to get out the binoculars

A walk around the varying habitats of the 405-hectare (1,000-acre) estate may be interrupted by the drumming of a woodpecker, the song of skylarks or the sound of a steam train travelling through the park. **Note**: Sheringham Hall is privately occupied. Limited access by written appointment with leaseholder.

Access:

Find out more: 01263 820550 or sheringhampark@nationaltrust.org.uk
nationaltrust.org.uk/sheringham

Sundon Hills Country Park

Upper Sundon, Bedfordshire 2000

Wildlife-rich chalk grassland, beech woodland, open meadows and a picnic site with views north towards the Greensand Ridge. **Note**: sorry no toilet. **Satnav**: use LU3 3PE.

Find out more: 01582 873663 or sundonhills@nationaltrust.org.uk

Sutton Hoo

Sutton Hoo, Woodbridge, Suffolk IP12 3DJ

1998

Sutton Hoo, Suffolk, offers breathtaking
exhibitions, above, and plenty of
space to explore, below

For 1,300 years Sutton Hoo's secrets were
hidden deep within a burial mound until, in
1939, a discovery was made which changed
history. From the sandy soil archaeologists
unearthed the imprint of a 27-metre-long
ship, its timbers long since rotted away.
This was revealed to be the ship burial of an
Anglo-Saxon king, complete with exquisite
gold and silver treasures. A stunning
full-size ship sculpture, newly designed
exhibitions, breathtaking replicas, the
atmospheric Royal Burial Ground and
a 17-metre-high viewing tower offering
stunning views over the landscape and
River Deben, all bring this fascinating story
to life. There is also a variety of walks on
the estate, including two new routes.

Access:

Find out more: 01394 389700 or
suttonhoo@nationaltrust.org.uk
nationaltrust.org.uk/sutton-hoo

Theatre Royal Bury St Edmunds

Westgate Street, Bury St Edmunds, Suffolk IP33 1QR 1974

Last surviving Regency playhouse in Britain, with a vibrant mixed programme. **Note**: managed by Bury St Edmunds Theatre Management Ltd.

Find out more: 01284 769505 or theatreroyal@nationaltrust.org.uk **nationaltrust.org.uk/theatre-royal**

Totternhoe Knolls

Castle Hill Road, Totternhoe, Bedfordshire 2000

The dramatic earthworks of a Norman castle rise from windswept chalk grassland. **Note**: sorry no toilet. **Satnav**: use LU6 1RG.

Find out more: 01582 873663 or totternhoeknolls@nationaltrust.org.uk

West Runton and Beeston Regis Heath

near West Runton, Norfolk 1925

A lovely place to walk among heath and woods, with fine views of the coast. **Note**: sorry no toilet. **Satnav**: use NR27 9ND.

Find out more: 01263 820550 or westrunton@nationaltrust.org.uk **nationaltrust.org.uk/west-runton-and-beeston-regis-heath**

Whipsnade Tree Cathedral

Whipsnade, Dunstable, Bedfordshire 1960

Peaceful place with trees planted in shape of medieval cathedral. Created after the First World War to commemorate fallen comrades. **Note**: annual service. **Satnav**: use LU6 2LQ.

Find out more: 01582 872406 or whipsnadetc@nationaltrust.org.uk **nationaltrust.org.uk/whipsnade-tree-cathedral**

Wicken Fen National Nature Reserve

near Ely, Cambridgeshire

1899

With vast skies above flowering meadows, sedge and reedbeds, Wicken Fen reveals a lost fenland landscape. A wealth of wildlife lives in this important wetland, including rarities such as hen harriers and bitterns, numerous dragonflies, moths and wildfowl. Changing every season, the fen feels wild, although people have shaped it for centuries; see how they lived and worked in the fenman's yard and cottage. The Wicken

Exploring the wetlands at Wicken Fen National Nature Reserve

Fen Vision, an ambitious landscape-scale conservation project, is opening new areas for wildlife and for exploration. Grazing herds of Highland cattle and Konik ponies help create a diverse range of new habitats. **Note**: some paths are seasonal. Charges apply for Wicken Lode boat trips (including members). **Satnav**: use CB7 5XP.

Access: ⬚⬚⬚⬚

Find out more: 01353 720274 or wickenfen@nationaltrust.org.uk
nationaltrust.org.uk/wicken

Willington Dovecote and Stables

Willington, Church End, near Bedford, Bedfordshire MK44 3PX 1914

One of the largest and best-preserved examples of a 16th-century stone dovecote, a remnant of Gostwick's extravagant manorial complex. **Note**: Dovecote and Stables can be viewed by appointment dependent on volunteer availability, contact Judy Endersby (01234 838278).

Find out more: 01480 499992 or willingtondovecote@nationaltrust.org.uk
nationaltrust.org.uk/willington-dovecote-and-stables

Wimpole Estate

Arrington, Royston, Cambridgeshire SG8 0BW

1976 ⬚⬚⬚⬚⬚⬚

A unique working estate, with an impressive mansion at its heart. Discover Wimpole's acres of parkland, miles of walks, vibrant walled kitchen garden and Home Farm. Explore the Hall, where intimate rooms contrast with beautiful Georgian interiors. With its various owners driven by passion and purpose, Wimpole is both a place to escape to and a place to get involved.

With an impressive mansion at its heart, Wimpole Estate, Cambridgeshire, is still very much a working estate

We continue the 3rd Earl of Hardwicke's passion for trail-blazing food production and design, celebrating the estate's past magnificence and echoing Elsie Bambridge's 20th-century revival. As owners changed, a roll-call of ingenious architects, artists and landscape designers shaped the estate. Wimpole is an 'all-year-round' place to visit, reflecting the changing seasons, with something to captivate and inspire all visitors. **Satnav**: follow the brown signs, entrance via A603.

Access: 🅿🅳♿🚻♿♿

Find out more: 01223 206000 or wimpole@nationaltrust.org.uk
nationaltrust.org.uk/wimpole

Discovering the Hall at Wimpole Estate

East Midlands

Rays of sunshine light up the landscape below Kinder Downfall:
Kinder, Edale and the High Peak, Derbyshire

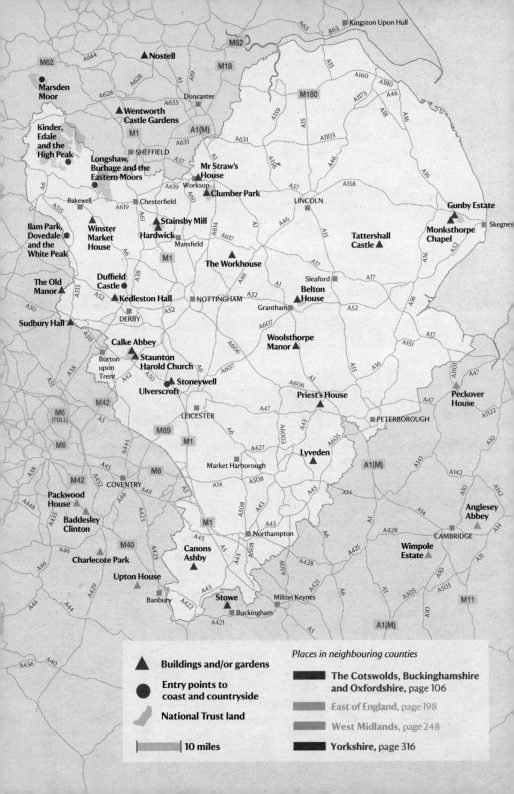

Kingston Upon Hull

M62

▲ Nostell

Marsden Moor

Wentworth Castle Gardens

Doncaster

Kinder, Edale and the High Peak

M1

SHEFFIELD

Longshaw, Burbage and the Eastern Moors

Mr Straw's House

Bakewell

Worksop

Chesterfield

▲ Clumber Park

LINCOLN

Gunby Estate

Skegness

Ilam Park, Dovedale and the White Peak

Winster Market House

▲ Stainsby Mill

Hardwick

Monksthorpe Chapel

Mansfield

Tattershall Castle ▲

The Old Manor

Duffield Castle

The Workhouse

Sudbury Hall

Kedleston Hall

NOTTINGHAM

Belton House

DERBY

Grantham

Sleaford

Calke Abbey

Woolsthorpe Manor

Staunton Harold Church

Burton upon Trent

Stoneywell

Ulverscroft

Priest's House

Peckover House

M42

LEICESTER

PETERBOROUGH

M6 (TOLL)

M69

M6

M1

Lyveden

A1(M)

Packwood House

Market Harborough

COVENTRY

M42

M6

Baddesley Clinton

Anglesey Abbey

CAMBRIDGE

Charlecote Park

Wimpole Estate

M40

Canons Ashby

Northampton

Upton House

Banbury

Stowe

Milton Keynes

Buckingham

M11

A1(M)

Legend:

▲ Buildings and/or gardens

● Entry points to coast and countryside

National Trust land

10 miles

Places in neighbouring counties

The Cotswolds, Buckinghamshire and Oxfordshire, page 106

East of England, page 198

West Midlands, page 248

Yorkshire, page 316

Belton House

near Grantham, Lincolnshire

1984 ⌂ ✝ ✿ ♨

Belton House sits elegantly in formal
gardens with views across pleasure grounds
and an ancient deer park. Although built
on a relatively modest scale, it has a
superlative collection of porcelain and
silver, a world-renowned library, and an
architectural finesse that reflects the wealth
and education of generations of the
Brownlow family. It's often cited as being

Belton House in Lincolnshire, above and below, sits in formal gardens with views across pleasure grounds

the perfect example of an English country house. In more recent times, Belton has become a popular destination for generations of families, with a huge adventure playground and seasonal activities, so there is something to do all year round. **Satnav:** use NG32 2LW.

Access: 🅿️ ♿ 🚹 ♿ 🚐

Find out more: 01476 566116 or belton@nationaltrust.org.uk Belton, near Grantham, Lincolnshire NG32 2LS **nationaltrust.org.uk/belton-house**

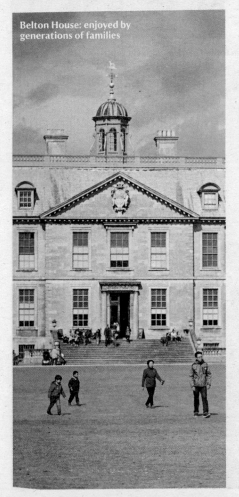
Belton House: enjoyed by generations of families

Calke Abbey

Ticknall, Derby, Derbyshire DE73 7JF

1985 🏛️ ✝️ 🍴 ♿ 🚐 🐾

Calke Abbey, Derbyshire, above and right: the most un-stately stately home imaginable

Poised somewhere between gentle neglect and downright dereliction, Calke Abbey, the un-stately home, is unlike other great country estates. Entering along the Lime Tree Avenue offers views of the historic parkland, home to ancient oaks, secluded ponds and woodland walks. The National Nature Reserve awaits discovery, and Calke Explore provides the perfect base to begin exploring the wider estate. Peeling paintwork and abandoned rooms tell the story of a country house in decline, while a vast collection reveals the varied interests of a loving family who never threw anything away. The walled garden offers moments of reflection, including a domed orangery and faded glasshouses, and beds bursting with seasonal produce and colour echo the history of Calke's working garden.

Access: 🅿️ ♿ 🚹 ♿ 🚐

Find out more: 01332 863822 or calkeabbey@nationaltrust.org.uk **nationaltrust.org.uk/calke**

The mansion at Canons Ashby, Northamptonshire, above, and exploring the grounds, below

Canons Ashby

near Daventry,
Northamptonshire NN11 3SD

1981 🏠✝🏛♻🎒

Access: ♿♿♿♿

Find out more: 01327 861900 or
canonsashby@nationaltrust.org.uk
nationaltrust.org.uk/canons-ashby

Ancient and peaceful, Canons Ashby is far removed from today's bustling lifestyle. Medieval canons built their priory near the small village of Ashby, but the Dissolution left a curiously truncated church and the village was lost, leaving nothing but mounds in the landscape. Nearby, the Elizabethan Dryden family built their home, making few changes during their 450 years of occupation. Victorian Sir Henry Dryden's curiosity led him to record the detail of the mansion, its unusual blend of architectural styles, mysterious wall-paintings, plasterwork and fine furnishings. Outside, lush gardens, parkland and ancient church offer space for tranquil contemplation.

Clumber Park

Worksop, Nottinghamshire S80 3BE

1946

Carved out of the ancient forest of Sherwood, a space of playfulness and pleasure on a grand scale was created by the Dukes of Newcastle. Clumber Park is true to its spirit as a place of recreation, with 20 miles of cycle routes and 1,537 hectares (3,800 acres) of parkland, woodland and heathland to explore. The beauty of the Gothic Revival chapel, with its original stained-glass windows, reveals a rich historic past. The Pleasure Grounds frame the magnificent lake, making a perfect place to stroll or picnic. The Walled Kitchen Garden, with its National Collection of Rhubarb, provides a variety of fruit and vegetables to the café, and there are colourful herbaceous borders during the summer.

Clumber Park in Nottinghamshire is a place of playfulness and pleasure on a grand scale

Gothic Revival chapel
at Clumber Park

Access: ⬜⬜⬜⬜⬜

Find out more: 01909 476592 or
clumberpark@nationaltrust.org.uk
nationaltrust.org.uk/clumber-park

Gunby Estate, Hall and Gardens

Gunby, Spilsby, Lincolnshire PE23 5SS

1944 ⬜⬜⬜⬜⬜

Set at the foot of the Lincolnshire Wolds.
Explore the 607-hectare (1,500-acre) estate
of the Massingberd family, who lived here
from 1700 until 1967. Find peace in the
large garden, where there is colour all year
with abundant spring flowers, summer
roses, autumn borders and plentiful fruit
and vegetables. **Satnav**: entrance is off
roundabout (not beyond or before).

Access: ⬜⬜⬜

Find out more: 01754 890102 or
gunbyhall@nationaltrust.org.uk
nationaltrust.org.uk/gunby-hall

Duffield Castle

Duffield, Derbyshire 1899

Site of one of England's largest medieval
castles – see its foundations, imagine the
stories and enjoy the Derbyshire views.
Note: sorry no toilet. Steep steps.
Satnav: use DE56 4DW.

Find out more: 01332 842191 or
duffieldcastle@nationaltrust.org.uk
nationaltrust.org.uk/duffield

Gunby Hall Estate: Monksthorpe Chapel

Monksthorpe, near Spilsby,
Lincolnshire PE23 5PP 2000

Monksthorpe Chapel, dated 1701, was made
to look like a barn to avoid detection and
features a rare open-air baptistry.

Find out more: 01754 890102 or
monksthorpe@nationaltrust.org.uk
nationaltrust.org.uk/monksthorpe-chapel

Hardwick

near Chesterfield, Derbyshire

1959

Scented blooms delight at Hardwick

One of the finest Elizabethan buildings in the country, Hardwick is a remarkable house, built by a remarkable woman. Full of architectural prowess, from the audaciously impressive glass windows, to the turrets standing proud, bearing the initials E.S., Elizabeth of Shrewsbury – also known as Bess of Hardwick. Inside, let the three floors take you on a journey, from the finest collections of Elizabethan tapestries and embroideries in Europe, to decadent and cosy Forties' furnishings. Relax while you

Glittering windows characterise Hardwick in Derbyshire

Hardwick Estate: Stainsby Mill

Doe Lea, Chesterfield, Derbyshire S44 5RW

1976

At this atmospheric gem on the Hardwick Estate, you can watch the Victorian water mill turn and see the cogs and machinery work to grind the flour as our millers still do. Pick up a bag of flour, then discover the surrounding parkland and Hardwick Hall. **Note**: nearest toilets and refreshments at Hardwick Hall.

Access:

Find out more: 01246 850430 or stainsbymill@nationaltrust.org.uk
nationaltrust.org.uk/stainsby-mill

Hardwick Estate: Stainsby Mill in Derbyshire

Enjoying Hardwick's Grade-I listed park, top, and blue bedroom, above

take in the gardens, which offer bright seasonal colour and unique surprises, including the herb garden full of scents, blossoming orchard and delightful rose garden. Surrounded by picturesque parkland and oak-scattered Grade I-listed woodland pasture, Hardwick overlooks Derbyshire's rolling hills, providing breathtaking views. **Note**: Old Hall owned by the National Trust and administered by English Heritage (01246 850431).
Satnav: use S44 5RW.

Access:

Find out more: 01246 850430 or hardwickhall@nationaltrust.org.uk
Doe Lea, near Chesterfield, Derbyshire S44 5QJ
nationaltrust.org.uk/hardwick

Ilam Park, Dovedale and the White Peak

Ilam, Ashbourne, Derbyshire

1934 ✝ 🏛 ⛴ ✿ 🐾 🐦

The Stepping Stones at Dovedale lead to a riverside walk through the National Nature Reserve full of caves and pinnacles, rich in wildlife and fossils. A 1½-mile walk across fields links Dovedale and Ilam Park, a tranquil parkland nestled beneath steep-sided hills on the River Manifold. The park is dotted with majestic mature trees and offers views of the church, the rugged backdrop of Thorpe Cloud and Bunster Hill. A 1-mile circular parkland route makes this a popular choice for families and dog walkers. The Church of the Holy Cross contains stories of St Bertram, buried within. **Note**: Ilam Hall is let to the Youth Hostel Association. Dovedale car park is privately owned and there is also a charge for toilets. **Satnav**: use DE6 2AZ.

Access: 🅿️ 🅿️ ♿ 📶 🚻 ♿

Find out more: 01335 350503 or peakdistrict@nationaltrust.org.uk **nationaltrust.org.uk/dovedale**

Ilam Park, Dovedale and the White Peak in Derbyshire

Kedleston Hall

near Derby, Derbyshire

1987 🏠✝✿🐾

Be inspired by a true 'temple of the arts' – as envisioned by celebrated architect Robert Adam. Experience the grandeur of this lavishly decorated 1760s show palace in Derbyshire, lived in over the centuries by the Curzon family, and explore the Eastern Museum of objects. Collected by Lord Curzon during his time as Viceroy of India, these represent the rich diversity of cultures and communities across South Asia. The mansion is set in 332 hectares (820 acres) of landscape parkland and Pleasure Grounds, which can be explored on foot all year. The parkland is popular for dog walks, picnics and orienteering. **Note**: the medieval All Saint's Church is managed by the Churches Conservation Trust. **Satnav**: for main entrance use DE22 5JD.

Access: 🅿️♿🚻🌳♿

Find out more: 01332 842191 or kedlestonhall@nationaltrust.org.uk Quarndon, near Derby, Derbyshire DE22 5JH **nationaltrust.org.uk/kedleston-hall**

Kedleston Hall in Derbyshire: the landscape parkland, above, and the hermitage, below

Kinder, Edale and the High Peak

near Hope Valley, Derbyshire

The High Peak, including Kinder, the Vale of Edale and along the Snake moors to the Derwent edges, offers exhilarating walks across heather moors, high gritstone edges and monumental windswept tors. Stories and wild nature abound amid the ancient peat bogs and quiet wooded cloughs. You can follow the route of the 1932 Mass Trespass onto Kinder Scout National Nature Reserve, retracing the steps of those early champions of access to wild places. Alternatively, a short walk up the steps of Mam Tor rewards you with panoramic views from this ancient hilltop fortress. **Note**: nearest toilets in villages and visitor centres (not Trust) at Ladybower Reservoir, Edale and Castleton.

Find out more: 01433 670368 or peakdistrict@nationaltrust.org.uk
nationaltrust.org.uk/kinder

Kinder, Edale and the High Peak, Derbyshire, above and below: exhilarating walks and fabulous views

Longshaw, Burbage and the Eastern Moors

near Sheffield, Derbyshire

1931

A countryside haven on Sheffield's doorstep, Longshaw, Burbage and the Eastern Moors has a network of footpaths and bridleways you can explore within a typical Peak District landscape of skies and silhouettes. Here you'll find long views, with scooping shapes of rocks and hills and gorges where water tumbles through ancient woods and over mossy boulders. A diverse range of wildlife lives peacefully here among abandoned millstones and packhorse routes of the past. The designed landscape around Longshaw Lodge, a former grouse-shooting estate, offers a warm and friendly starting point for your adventure.

Longshaw, Burbage and the Eastern Moors, Derbyshire, above and top: countryside haven

Note: National Trust/RSPB manage Eastern Moors for Peak District National Park; Burbage for Sheffield County Council. **Satnav**: use S11 7TZ (follow brown signs).

Access:

Find out more: 01433 631757 (Longshaw). 0114 289 1543 (Eastern Moors) or peakdistrict@nationaltrust.org.uk **nationaltrust.org.uk/longshaw**

Lyveden

Harley Way, near Oundle,
Northamptonshire PE8 5AT

1922

Deep in Northamptonshire lies a mysterious garden. Begun by Sir Thomas Tresham in 1595 but never completed, the house stands as testament to his Catholicism. Persecuted for his religious beliefs, Sir Thomas sought solace in the creation of his garden. New facilities opening in spring reveal the intriguing story behind Lyveden and provide the opportunity for lunch or cake in our new café. For the first time you can discover the wonder of this Elizabethan garden in the order originally intended, as grass paths, viewing mounts and moats lead you upwards from manor house to the symbolic garden lodge.

Access:

Find out more: 01832 205259 or
lyveden@nationaltrust.org.uk
nationaltrust.org.uk/lyveden

Lyveden, above and below, a mysterious Elizabethan garden and lodge deep in Northamptonshire

Mr Straw's House

5–7 Blyth Grove, Worksop,
Nottinghamshire S81 0JG

Mr Straw's House,
Nottinghamshire:
untouched time capsule

Within the Sanderson-papered walls
of this middle-class home, the family
lived thriftily, installing few modern
conveniences since 1923. A large and
intriguing collection of everyday objects
and personal papers has survived alongside
traces of the occasional indulgence.
The lovingly tended garden and orchard
include a cacti collection and fruit trees.

Access: 🏃

Find out more: 01909 482380 or
mrstrawshouse@nationaltrust.org.uk
nationaltrust.org.uk/mr-straws-house

The Old Manor

Norbury, Ashbourne, Derbyshire DE6 2ED
1987

An idyllic medieval hall featuring a rare
king post and well-preserved Tudor door,
set within beautiful gardens.

Find out more: 01283 585337 or
oldmanor@nationaltrust.org.uk
nationaltrust.org.uk/old-manor

Priest's House, Easton on the Hill

38 West Street, Easton on the Hill, near
Stamford, Northamptonshire PE9 3LS 1966

Delightful small late 15th-century building;
interesting local architecture and museum.

Find out more: 01832 205158 or
priestshouse2@nationaltrust.org.uk
**nationaltrust.org.uk/priests-house-
easton-on-the-hill**

Staunton Harold Church

Staunton Harold Estate, Ashby-de-la-
Zouch, Leicestershire LE65 1RW 1954

Rare, imposing 1653 church; landscape lake
and wooded hills beyond. **Note**: nearest
toilet 500 yards (not National Trust).

Find out more: 01332 863822 or
stauntonharold@nationaltrust.org.uk
**nationaltrust.org.uk/staunton-harold-
church**

Stoneywell

Whitcroft's Lane, Ulverscroft,
Leicestershire LE67 9QE

2012 🏠 ✳️

Zigzagging from its rocky outcrop,
Stoneywell is the realisation of one man's
Arts and Crafts vision within a family home.
Original furniture and family treasures fill
the cottage's quirky rooms and, outside,
every turn conjures childhood memories
of holiday excitement – one way to the fort,
another to the woods beyond.

Access: 🅿️ ♿ 🎫

Find out more: 01530 248040 (Infoline).
01530 248048 (bookings) or
stoneywell@nationaltrust.org.uk
nationaltrust.org.uk/stoneywell

Stoneywell, Leicestershire: Arts and Crafts vision

Sudbury Hall and the National Trust Museum of Childhood

Sudbury, Ashbourne, Derbyshire DE6 5HT

1967 🏠 ✳️

Fun at Sudbury Hall and the National Trust Museum of Childhood in Derbyshire

A complete day out, with two unique
experiences in one location. The Hall has
one of the most surprising, light and
beautiful long galleries in England and is
the result of George Vernon's aspirations
to create a perfect new home. Enjoy the
way the magnificent interiors, including
exuberant plasterwork and Grinling
Gibbons woodcarving, breathe the spirit
of the Restoration through their fineness,
delicacy and touches of humour.

The museum is a place of fun and fascination for all ages. You can discover about childhood from the Victorian period to the present day; send your little one up a chimney, play with our hands-on toys and games and experience the Victorian Schoolroom.

Access: 🅿️ ♿ ♿ 🚻 ♿ ♿

Find out more: 01283 585337 or sudburyhall@nationaltrust.org.uk
nationaltrust.org.uk/sudbury-hall-and-museum-of-childhood

Sudbury Hall and the National Trust Museum of Childhood: inside the Hall, below, and its elegant exterior

Tattershall Castle

Sleaford Road, Tattershall,
Lincolnshire LN4 4LR

| 1925 |

Rising proudly from the flat Lincolnshire
fens, Tattershall Castle was designed to
display wealth, position and power. Built by
Lord Ralph Cromwell, Treasurer of England,
the Great Tower is one of the earliest and
finest surviving examples of English
medieval brickwork. Dramatically saved
from being dismantled and exported, the
castle and its huge Gothic fireplaces were
restored from ruin by Lord Curzon of
Kedleston between 1912 and 1914. Imagine
the splendour of this once-palatial private
residence as you wander through the vast
echoing chambers. Ascend the spiral
staircase from basement to battlements
and take in spectacular views of the
countryside. **Note**: access to the tower
via a spiral staircase only (149 steps).
Loose gravel paths throughout.

Access:

Find out more: 01526 342543 or
tattershallcastle@nationaltrust.org.uk
nationaltrust.org.uk/tattershall

**Tattershall Castle rises proudly
from the flat Lincolnshire fenland**

Exquisite plasterwork
at Tattershall Castle

Ulverscroft Nature Reserve

near Copt Oak, Loughborough,
Leicestershire | 1945 |

Nestled in the ancient Charnwood Forest,
the heathland and woodland habitats of
Ulverscroft support a rich variety of wildlife.
Note: sorry no toilet.
Satnav: use LE67 9QE.

Find out more: 01332 863822 or
ulverscroftreserve@nationaltrust.org.uk
nationaltrust.org.uk/ulverscroft

Winster Market House

Main Street, Winster, Matlock,
Derbyshire DE4 2DJ | 1906 |

A small listed 16th-century Market House
with displays upstairs – the first Derbyshire
place acquired by the National Trust,
costing £50. **Note**: unstaffed.

Find out more: 01335 350503 or
winstermarkethouse@nationaltrust.org.uk
**nationaltrust.org.uk/winster-market-
house**

Woolsthorpe Manor

Water Lane, Woolsthorpe by Colsterworth, near Grantham, Lincolnshire NG33 5PD

1943 🏠 ❀

The world changed here. Isaac Newton, scientist, mathematician, thinker, craftsman, was born and grew up at Woolsthorpe Manor, doing much of his most important scientific work before he was 26. Sent home from Cambridge by the plague during 1665-7, he experimented obsessively, laying foundations for a groundbreaking scientific revolution. Here he split sunlight into colours with a prism and an apple fell from a tree to inspire his theory of gravity. Newton's genius still resonates through our world and for more than 300 years people have come to walk in his footsteps and be inspired by his story.

Access: 🅿️ 🅳 🕍 🅰️ ♿

Find out more: 01476 860338 or woolsthorpemanor@nationaltrust.org.uk
nationaltrust.org.uk/woolsthorpe

The birthplace of Isaac Newton, Woolsthorpe Manor in Lincolnshire, above and below, was the site of ground-breaking scientific discoveries

The Workhouse, Southwell

Southwell, Nottinghamshire

2002 🏠✛

Walking up the paupers' path towards The Workhouse, it is easy to imagine how the Victorian poor might have felt as they sought refuge here. This austere building, the most complete workhouse in existence, was built in 1824 as a place of last resort for the destitute. Its architecture was influenced by prison design, and its harsh regime became a blueprint for workhouses throughout the country. The stories of people who lived and worked here over the years help tell the history of the building's evolution and prompt reflection on how society has tackled social welfare through time. **Satnav**: use NG25 0QB.

Access: ♿♿♿♿

Find out more: 01636 817260 or theworkhouse@nationaltrust.org.uk
Upton Road, Southwell,
Nottinghamshire NG25 0PT
nationaltrust.org.uk/southwell-workhouse

The Workhouse, Southwell, Nottinghamshire, above and below: the last resort for the truly desperate

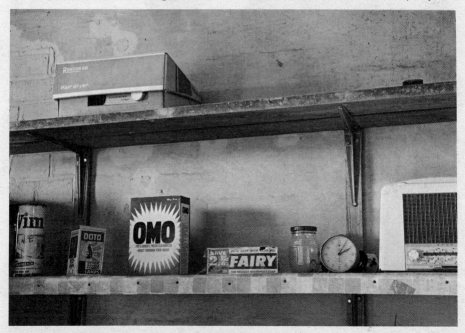

The curious rock formations at
Kinver Edge and the Rock Houses, Staffordshire

West Midlands

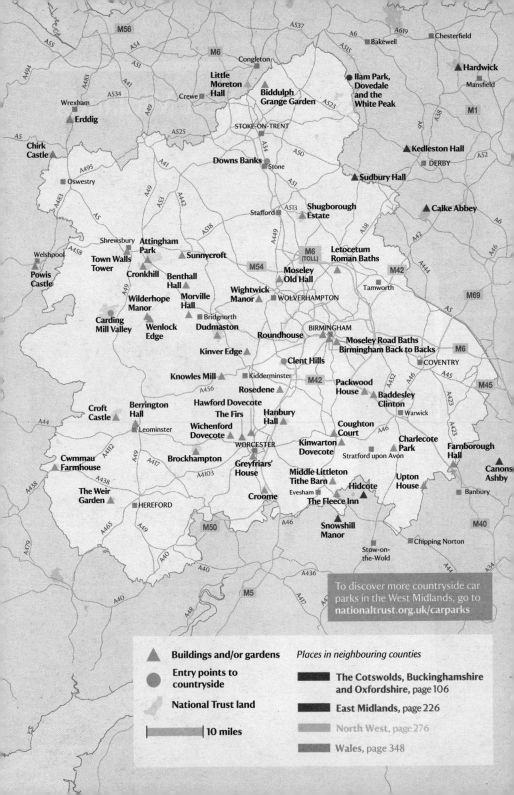

M56
M6
M6
M1
A537
A6
A619
A5
A55
A54
A55
A494
A51
Chesterfield
Congleton
Little
Moreton
Hall
Bakewell
A6
A5
Hardwick
A483
A41
Biddulph
Grange Garden
Ilam Park,
Dovedale
and the
White Peak
Mansfield
Crewe
Wrexham
A534
A523
Erddig
A51
A49
STOKE-ON-TRENT
A38
A6
A525
A52
A5
Chirk
Castle
Kedleston Hall
Downs Banks
A50
Oswestry
A495
A34
A51
DERBY
Stone
A513
A52
A483
A53
A42
A49
A442
Stafford
Shugborough
Estate
Sudbury Hall
Calke Abbey
A5
A6
Shrewsbury
Attingham
Park
Sunnycroft
A518
Letocetum
Roman Baths
A46
A458
Welshpool
Town Walls
Tower
A449
M6
(TOLL)
M42
A444
M69
Powis
Castle
Cronkhill
Benthall
Hall
M54
Moseley
Old Hall
Tamworth
A49
Wilderhope
Manor
Morville
Hall
Wightwick
Manor
WOLVERHAMPTON
A5
Carding
Mill Valley
Wenlock
Edge
Dudmaston
Bridgnorth
BIRMINGHAM
Roundhouse
Moseley Road Baths
Birmingham Back to Backs
M6
Kinver Edge
Clent Hills
COVENTRY
Knowles Mill
Kidderminster
M42
Packwood
House
A452
A46
M45
Croft
Castle
Berrington
Hall
Rosedene
A456
Baddesley
Clinton
A45
M42
A423
A44
Hawford Dovecote
The Firs
Hanbury
Hall
Warwick
Leominster
Wichenford
Dovecote
WORCESTER
Coughton
Court
A46
Charlecote
Park
Farnborough
Hall
A4112
Cwmmau
Farmhouse
A417
Brockhampton
Kinwarton
Dovecote
Stratford upon Avon
A423
Canons
Ashby
A438
A4103
Greyfriars'
House
Middle Littleton
Tithe Barn
Upton
House
Banbury
The Weir
Garden
A49
Croome
Hidcote
M40
HEREFORD
Evesham
The Fleece Inn
A465
A49
M50
A46
Snowshill
Manor
Chipping Norton
A479
A40
Stow-on-
the-Wold
M40
A34
M5
A436
A44
A40
A417
M5
A48

To discover more countryside car
parks in the West Midlands, go to
nationaltrust.org.uk/carparks

▲ Buildings and/or gardens

● Entry points to
countryside

National Trust land

|———————| 10 miles

Places in neighbouring counties

**The Cotswolds, Buckinghamshire
and Oxfordshire**, page 106

East Midlands, page 226

North West, page 276

Wales, page 348

Attingham Park

Atcham, Shrewsbury, Shropshire SY4 4TP

1947 🏠 ❀ ♨

Attingham inspires a sense of beauty, space and awe. From the moment you enter the gates, views open up across the 200-year-old parkland towards the Shropshire Hills and the impressive mansion emerges against silhouettes of cedar trees. The house, which sits at the heart of Lord Berwick's estate, is an example of classical design and Italian influence. Outside, cattle graze and fallow deer roam, woodland glades of historic trees offer peace and shade, while the red-brick organic walled garden is a place of order, productivity and horticulture. The accessible paths around the parkland are perfect for walks, running or exploring the 1,619-hectare (4,000-acre) estate. Full of life and locally loved, there's something for everyone all year round.

Access: 🅿️ 🚻 ♿ ♿ ♿

Find out more: 01743 708123 (Infoline). 01743 708162 or attingham@nationaltrust.org.uk
nationaltrust.org.uk/attingham-park

Awe-inspiring Attingham Park in Shropshire, above and below, is a place of beauty, peace and space

Attingham Park Estate: Cronkhill

near Atcham, Shrewsbury,
Shropshire SY5 6JP 1947

Delightful picturesque Italianate hillside villa designed by Regency architect John Nash, with beautiful views across the Attingham Estate. **Note**: house ground floor, garden and stables open as part of visit. Property contents belong to tenant.

Find out more: 01743 708162 or cronkhill@nationaltrust.org.uk
nationaltrust.org.uk/attingham-park-cronkhill

Attingham Park Estate: Town Walls Tower

Shrewsbury, Shropshire SY1 1TN 1930

This last remaining 14th-century watchtower sits on what were once the medieval fortified, defensive walls of Shrewsbury. **Note**: sorry no toilet and 40 extremely steep, narrow steps to top floor.

Find out more: 01743 708162 or townwallstower@nationaltrust.org.uk
nationaltrust.org.uk/town-walls-tower

Baddesley Clinton

Rising Lane, Baddesley Clinton,
Warwickshire B93 0DQ

1980

Atmospheric Baddesley Clinton in Warwickshire, above right and right: a sanctuary for centuries

The magic of Baddesley Clinton comes from its secluded, timeless setting deep within its own parkland. From refuge to haven, this atmospheric moated manor house has been a sanctuary since the 15th century. Discover Baddesley's late medieval, Tudor and 20th-century histories and uncover its stories, from hiding persecuted Catholics in its priest's holes, to the history of the Ferrers family who lived at Baddesley for more than 500 years. The peaceful gardens include fish pools, walled garden and a lakeside walk, perfect for a tranquil stroll.

Access: 🅿♿🚾📶♿

Find out more: 01564 783294 or baddesleyclinton@nationaltrust.org.uk
nationaltrust.org.uk/baddesley-clinton

Benthall Hall

Broseley, Shropshire TF12 5RX

1958 🏠✝♿🚲

Benthall Hall, Shropshire, has been home to the same family since Saxon times

Within this fine stone house, discover the history of the Benthall family from the Saxon period to the present day. Outside, the garden includes a beautiful Restoration church, a restored plantsman's garden with pretty crocus displays in spring and autumn, and an old kitchen garden.

Access: 🅿♿♿🚾📶

Find out more: 01952 882159 or benthall@nationaltrust.org.uk
nationaltrust.org.uk/benthall

Berrington Hall, Herefordshire, sits within 'Capability' Brown's final garden and landscape, and contains jewel-like interiors, below

Berrington Hall

near Leominster, Herefordshire HR6 0DW

1957 🏛 ✿ ♿ 🐾

Standing proud and strong, this fine Georgian mansion sits within 'Capability' Brown's final garden and landscape. In the house are jewel-like interiors, designed by Henry Holland and home to the Harley, Rodney and Cawley families. Upstairs you can explore the life of Ann Bangham, wife of Thomas Harley, and see a dress fit for a king. Learn more about the Berrington Garden Project, nurture your mind and body with a walk round the lake and discover the story behind the eating apple, including the historic varieties still growing in Berrington's garden.

Note: major restoration to mansion stonework and garden paths and walls.

Access: 🅿 🅳 ♿ 🎵 ♿ 🚻

Find out more: 01568 615721 or berrington@nationaltrust.org.uk
nationaltrust.org.uk/berrington-hall

Biddulph Grange Garden

Grange Road, Biddulph,
Staffordshire ST8 7SD

1988 🏵

Biddulph Grange Garden is a remarkable survival, a formal Victorian horticultural masterpiece and a quirky, playful paradise full of intrigue and surprise. Created by its visionary owner, James Bateman, the garden and Geological Gallery express his attempts to reconcile his religious convictions with his passion for botany and geology. His plant and fossil collections come from all over the world – a visit takes you on a journey from an Italian terrace to an Egyptian pyramid, via a Himalayan glen and Chinese garden, hidden by tunnels, hedges and rockwork. The collection includes rhododendrons, Wellingtonias and the oldest golden larch in Britain.

Note: there are 400 steps in the garden.

Access: 🅿♿♿🚾♿

Find out more: 01782 517999 or biddulphgrange@nationaltrust.org.uk
nationaltrust.org.uk/biddulph-grange-garden

Biddulph Grange Garden, Staffordshire, above and below: playful paradise and horticultural masterpiece

Birmingham

Birmingham Back to Backs

55-63 Hurst Street/50-54 Inge Street, Birmingham, West Midlands B5 4TE

2004

Immerse yourself in the life of residents at Birmingham's last surviving court of back to backs and get an insight into how people lived from the 1840s to the 1970s. With privies, coal fires, candlelight and cramped spaces, you'll get a real taste of back-to-back life. **Note**: eight flights of steep, winding stairs.

Access:

Immerse yourself in a lost world at
Birmingham Back to Backs, above and left

Find out more: 0121 666 7671 (booking line)
or backtobacks@nationaltrust.org.uk
**nationaltrust.org.uk/birmingham-back-
to-backs**

Clent Hills

near Romsley, Worcestershire

See page 261.

Moseley Road Baths

497 Moseley Road, Balsall Heath,
Birmingham B12 9BX

Swim in beauty – this internationally
significant Grade II*-listed swimming pool
has been open for community swimming
since 1907. **Note**: run as a coalition with
Birmingham City Council, Historic England,
World Monuments Fund and swimming
managed by Moseley Road Baths
Charitable Incorporated Organisation.

Find out more: 0121 439 0320 or
moseleyroadbaths.org.uk

Roundhouse

Sheepcote Street, Birmingham B16 8AE

| 2017 | 🏠 |

This unique horseshoe-shaped building, a
curious survivor, lies at the heart of
Birmingham's canals and is an ideal base
from which to explore the city by foot, bike
or boat. **Note**: Roundhouse Birmingham is
a partnership with Canal & River Trust.

Access: 🗺️ 📖

Find out more:
hello@roundhousebirmingham.org.uk
**nationaltrust.org.uk/roundhouse-
birmingham**

Roundhouse: curious horseshoe-shaped building

Brockhampton

Bringsty, near Bromyard,
Herefordshire WR6 5TB

1946 🏠✝🔆🌸🎭

More than 600 years ago the Dumbleton
family built this moated manor house
tucked away in a Herefordshire valley. Find
out about the lives of the people who lived
here and discover how a once-grand
medieval hall was slowly transformed into
a modest home for farmers. In the wider
estate there are walks through a farming
landscape with parkland, hidden dingles,
gushing streams and wild woodlands
waiting to be discovered. Join us as we
replant lost Victorian orchards and explore
the origins of the humble apple in new
outdoor 'orchard rooms', created in
partnership with the local community.
Note: some walks include challenging
terrain with steep slopes and muddy areas.

Access: 🅿♿🚻💺🚽♿

Find out more: 01885 482077 or
brockhampton@nationaltrust.org.uk
nationaltrust.org.uk/brockhampton

Moated Brockhampton in Herefordshire,
above and below, changed over the centuries from
a grand medieval hall to a modest farmer's home

Carding Mill Valley and the Long Mynd

near Church Stretton, Shropshire

1965

Carding Mill Valley and the Long Mynd, Shropshire

At Carding Mill Valley you are suddenly in the heart of wild countryside. Here families can enjoy playing in the stream, a variety of walks and exploring. From the valley, head up to the top of the Long Mynd and be rewarded with views of Shropshire and beyond. **Satnav**: use SY6 6JG.

Access:

Find out more: 01694 725000 or cardingmill@nationaltrust.org.uk
nationaltrust.org.uk/carding-mill-valley-and-the-long-mynd

Charlecote Park

Wellesbourne, Warwick,
Warwickshire CV35 9ER

1946

Charlecote Park was already in its middle age when Elizabeth I arrived 450 years ago, entering through the gatehouse and on to the welcoming red-brick mansion, just as you will today. A family home for more than eight centuries, it is a place of surprising treasures, with collections reflecting the tastes, lifestyle and varied fortunes of the Lucy family. Imagine the hum of activity of a working estate in the domestic 'below-stairs' spaces and in the laundry room and brewhouse in the courtyard. In the stables

The garden at Charlecote Park, Warwickshire

see the family's carriage collection, while in the parkland Jacob sheep and fallow deer roam across the 'Capability' Brown landscape, a haven for wildlife in which you can picnic and play, walk and wander.

Access: ▣▣▣▣▣▣

Find out more: 01789 470277 or charlecotepark@nationaltrust.org.uk **nationaltrust.org.uk/charlecote**

The welcoming red-brick mansion at Charlecote Park, below, and resident deer, above

Clent Hills

near Romsley, Worcestershire

1959

Set on the edge of Birmingham and the Black Country, this green oasis with panoramic views is the perfect place for a refreshing walk or a picnic on a sunny day. Families can create their own adventures – building dens, hunting for geocaches or simply getting closer to nature. **Note**: nearest facilities at Nimmings Wood entrance. **Satnav**: use B62 0NL for Nimmings Wood entrance.

Access:

Find out more: 01562 887912 or clenthills@nationaltrust.org.uk
nationaltrust.org.uk/clent-hills

View from the Clent Hills, Worcestershire

Coughton Court

Alcester, Warwickshire B49 5JA

1946

Coughton Court, Warwickshire, above and top: faith, perseverance and intrigue

Coughton has been home to the Throckmorton family for more than 600 years. Facing persecution for their Catholic faith, they were willing to risk everything. You can discover their story and find out about a family's struggles, perseverance and intrigues, including their link to the infamous Gunpowder Plot. Coughton is very much a family home with an intimate feel. The Throckmorton family still live here and they created and manage the gardens, including a riverside walk, bog garden and beautiful display of roses in the walled garden. **Note**: picnics welcome in the three fenced picnic areas only (none in the formal gardens please).

Access: ⬚⬚⬚⬚⬚

Find out more: 01789 400777 or coughtoncourt@nationaltrust.org.uk
nationaltrust.org.uk/coughton-court

Spectacular borders at Coughton Court: created and managed by the Throckmorton family

Croft Castle and Parkland

near Leominster, Herefordshire

1957 ⬚⬚⬚⬚⬚⬚⬚

Croft Castle and Parkland in Herefordshire

This intimate house became the Croft family home before the Domesday Book. Its walls conceal a rich and turbulent history, with many compelling 20th-century stories to uncover. The interiors, styled by Thomas Farnolls Pritchard, also tell an 18th- and 19th-century tale. You can take your dog for a stroll to the Iron Age hill fort, exploring the historic parkland with ancient trees along the way, and discover new views and walks in Fishpool Valley as we continue our restoration project. Croft Castle is a place to immerse yourself in 1,000 years of power, politics and pleasure.
Satnav: use HR6 0BL.

Access: 🅿️ 🄳 ♨️ ♿ ♿

Find out more: 01568 780246 or
croftcastle@nationaltrust.org.uk   Yarpole,
near Leominster, Herefordshire HR6 9PW
nationaltrust.org.uk/croft-castle

**Croft Castle, above and below,
conceals a rich and turbulent history**

Croome

near High Green, Worcester,
Worcestershire WR8 9DW

1996   🏠 ✝️ ♿ ♨️

There's more than meets the eye at
Croome. A secret wartime airbase, now a
visitor centre and museum, was once a hub
of activity for thousands of people. Outside
is the grandest of English landscapes,
'Capability' Brown's masterful first
commission, with commanding views over
the Malverns. The parkland, nearly lost but

**Graceful swans and an accessible path
at Croome in Worcestershire**

now restored, is great for walks and adventures with a surprise around every corner. At the heart of the park lies Croome Court, once home to the Earls of Coventry. The 6th Earl was an 18th-century trendsetter, and today Croome follows his lead, using artists and craftspeople to tell the story of its eclectic past in inventive ways. **Note**: walled gardens, privately owned. **Satnav**: follow signs from main road, not satnav.

Access:

Find out more: 01905 371006 or croome@nationaltrust.org.uk **nationaltrust.org.uk/croome**

Wintry walk, below, and Croome Court, right

Cwmmau Farmhouse

Brilley, Whitney-on-Wye,
Herefordshire HR3 6JP 1965

A charming 17th-century timbered
farmhouse with many original features and
stunning views across Herefordshire.

Find out more: 01568 780246 or
cwmmaufarmhouse@nationaltrust.org.uk
nationaltrust.org.uk/cwmmau-farmhouse

Downs Banks

Washdale Lane, Oulton Heath,
near Stone, Staffordshire 1950

A little wilderness of woodlands and
heath, with easy access walks, in the heart
of the Midlands. **Note**: sorry no toilet.
Some steep paths.

Find out more: 01889 880160 or
downsbanks@nationaltrust.org.uk
nationaltrust.org.uk/downs-banks

Dudmaston

Quatt, near Bridgnorth,
Shropshire WV15 6QN

1978

Stretching across 1,214 hectares (3,000
acres) of ancient woodland and park,
Dudmaston is a working estate with a
family home at its heart. Steeped in history
but shaped by modern tastes and radical
thinking, it is a delightful collision of
unexpected contrasts. From the
picturesque dingle, to the remarkable
pieces by Moore and Matisse in the
galleries, art has always found a home here.
Discover modern sculpture in the garden or
find a tranquil spot to take in the views over
the pool. Explore the wider estate all year,
with walks from Comer Woods, Hampton
Loade and Sawmill. **Note**: the family home
of Mr and Mrs Mark Hamilton-Russell.

Dudmaston, Shropshire: a much-loved family home

Dudmaston's glorious grounds are a joy to explore

Access: 🅿️♿🚻🚶♿

Find out more: 01746 780866 or
dudmaston@nationaltrust.org.uk
nationaltrust.org.uk/dudmaston

The Firs – Birthplace of Edward Elgar

Crown East Lane, Lower Broadheath,
Worcester, Worcestershire WR2 6RH

2017 🏛️ ❀

Family treasures tell the story of Sir Edward

Elgar's humble beginnings in the family
cottage. Learn more about Elgar's
inspiration in the modern visitor centre
(three exhibition spaces). Outside, the
cottage garden is the perfect place to sit
and reflect on the life of this great
composer and his works.

Access: 🅿️♿🚻🚶♿

Find out more: 01905 333330 or
thefirs@nationaltrust.org.uk
nationaltrust.org.uk/the-firs

Farnborough Hall

Farnborough, near Banbury,
Warwickshire OX17 1DU 1960

Carolean house with exquisite plasterwork
and grand stairway. Set in landscaped
gardens with a mile-long terrace walk and
parkland views. **Note:** occupied and
administered by the Holbech family.

Find out more: 01295 670266 (option six)
or farnboroughhall@nationaltrust.org.uk
nationaltrust.org.uk/farnborough

The Fleece Inn

Bretforton, near Evesham,
Worcestershire WR11 7JE
1978

Medieval half-timbered longhouse,
now a traditional village inn, with barn
and orchard. Known for folk music,
Morris dancing and asparagus.

Find out more: 01386 831173 or
fleeceinn@nationaltrust.org.uk
nationaltrust.org.uk/fleece-inn

Greyfriars' House and Garden

Friar Street, Worcester,
Worcestershire WR1 2LZ

1966 🏠🌸

Set in the heart of historic Worcester, this timber-framed house, built in the 1490s, reflected the fortunes of its surroundings for centuries until it was rescued and carefully restored by the Matley-Moores. Now you can explore 500 years of history through the lens of an unusual brother and sister.

Access: 🏛

Find out more: 01905 23571 or greyfriars@nationaltrust.org.uk
nationaltrust.org.uk/greyfriars

Greyfriars' House and Garden in Worcestershire

Hanbury Hall

School Road, Hanbury, Droitwich Spa,
Worcestershire WR9 7EA

 1953 🏠🌸♿

Elegant parterre at Hanbury Hall, Worcestershire

A country retreat in the heart of Worcestershire. The house and garden, originally a stage-set for summer parties, offer a glimpse into life at the turn of the 18th century. Don't miss the original wall-paintings by Sir James Thornhill; full of drama and politics, they show the birth of Georgian society. The original formal gardens, designed by George London, have been faithfully recreated and complement the relaxed later gardens, with orangery, orchards and walled garden. If you venture further afield, our walks into the parkland will lead you into the remains of ancient forests and historic avenues.

Hanbury Hall: the original party house

Access: 🅿️ 🅳 🅴 ♿ ♿ 🚻

Find out more: 01527 821214 or
hanburyhall@nationaltrust.org.uk
nationaltrust.org.uk/hanbury-hall

Hawford Dovecote

Hawford, Worcestershire WR3 7SG 1973

Picturesque dovecote, which has survived
virtually unaltered since the late 16th
century, retaining many nesting boxes.
Note: sorry no toilet or tea-room. Please
park carefully to one side of Chatley Lane
without obstructing any private access.

Find out more: 01527 821214 or
hawforddovecote@nationaltrust.org.uk
nationaltrust.org.uk/hawford-dovecote

Kinver Edge and the Rock Houses

near Stourbridge, Staffordshire

1917 🏛️🏚️😊♿

At the Holy Austin Rock Houses discover
surprisingly cosy homes carved into the
rock of an imposing sandstone ridge. Walks
in the surrounding countryside of Kinver
Edge cross open heathland, buzzing with
wildlife, and woodland trails leading to
further rock houses nestled among the
trees. Dramatic views across three counties.
Satnav: use DY7 6DL for Rock Houses.

Access: 🅿️ 🚶

**Kinver Edge and the Rock Houses, Staffordshire,
below and right: surprisingly cosy**

Find out more: 01384 872553 or
kinveredge@nationaltrust.org.uk
Holy Austin Rock Houses, Compton Road,
Kinver, near Stourbridge,
Staffordshire DY7 6DL
nationaltrust.org.uk/kinver-edge

Kinwarton Dovecote

Kinwarton, near Alcester,
Warwickshire B49 6HB [1958]

Rare 14th-century circular dovecote with
metre-thick walls, hundreds of nesting holes
and original rotating ladder. **Note**: livestock
may be grazing. Sorry no toilet.

Find out more: 01789 400777 or
kinwartondovecote@nationaltrust.org.uk
nationaltrust.org.uk/kinwarton-dovecote

Knowles Mill

Dowles Brook, Bewdley,
Worcestershire DY12 2LX [1938]

Dating from the 18th century, the mill
retains much of its machinery, including
the frames of an overshot waterwheel.
Note: Mill Cottage not open to visitors
(please respect the resident's privacy).
Sorry no toilet.

Find out more: 01527 821214 or
knowlesmill@nationaltrust.org.uk
nationaltrust.org.uk/knowles-mill

Letocetum Roman Baths and Museum

Watling Street, Wall, near Lichfield,
Staffordshire WS14 0AW [1934]

Open-air remains of a once-important
Roman staging post and settlement,
including *mansio* (Roman inn) and
bathhouse. **Note**: in the guardianship
of English Heritage.

Find out more: 0370 333 1181 (English
Heritage) or letocetum@nationaltrust.org.uk
nationaltrust.org.uk/letocetum-roman-baths

Middle Littleton Tithe Barn

Middle Littleton, Evesham,
Worcestershire WR11 8LN [1975]

The largest and finest restored
13th-century tithe barn in the country.
Note: sorry no toilet.

Find out more: 01905 371006 or
middlelittleton@nationaltrust.org.uk
nationaltrust.org.uk/middle-littleton-tithe-barn

Morville Hall

Morville, near Bridgnorth,
Shropshire WV16 5NB [1965]

Elizabethan gem with a Georgian
makeover. Enchanting gardens spill
down to the Mor Brook against the
backdrop of the Shropshire Hills.

Note: property contents are a mix of items on loan and tenant's own.

Find out more: 01746 780866 (Dudmaston Hall) or morvillehall@nationaltrust.org.uk
nationaltrust.org.uk/morville-hall

Moseley Old Hall

Moseley Old Hall Lane, Fordhouses, Wolverhampton, Staffordshire WV10 7HY

1962

Moseley Old Hall, Staffordshire:
intricate knot garden

This atmospheric farmhouse, built circa 1600, holds many secrets. Charles II hid here after escaping the 1651 Battle of Worcester. Inside, a log fire crackles as 17th-century domestic life surrounds you. Outside, explore the walled garden, containing herbs and vegetables, the orchard and knot garden. Beyond is King's Walk Wood.

Access:

Find out more: 01902 782808 or moseleyoldhall@nationaltrust.org.uk
nationaltrust.org.uk/moseley-old-hall

Packwood House

Packwood Lane, Lapworth, Warwickshire B94 6AT

1941

Surrounded by beautiful gardens and countryside, Packwood was described by a guest in the 1930s as 'a house to dream of, a garden to dream in'. Lovingly restored at the beginning of the 20th century by Graham Baron Ash, you can discover the detail behind the man, his passion for collecting and his collection. The gardens include brightly coloured, 'mingled style' herbaceous borders, famous sculpted yews and an 18th-century gentleman's kitchen garden.

Packwood House, Warwickshire:
'A house to dream of, a garden to dream in'

The famous yews at Packwood House, top, and the kitchen garden, above

Access: [P] [D] [symbols] [&]

Find out more: 01564 782024 or
packwood@nationaltrust.org.uk
nationaltrust.org.uk/packwood

Rosedene

Victoria Road, Dodford, near Bromsgrove,
Worcestershire B61 9BU [1997]

Restored 1840s cottage with an organic
garden and orchard, illustrating the
mid-19th-century Chartist movement.
Note: available to hire as a 'back to basics'
holiday cottage.

Find out more: 01527 821214 or
rosedene@nationaltrust.org.uk
nationaltrust.org.uk/rosedene

Shugborough Estate

Milford, near Stafford,
Staffordshire ST17 0UP

[1966] [symbols]

**Shugborough Estate, Staffordshire:
the elegant Georgian mansion**

Shaped by its illustrious and maritime
history, Shugborough embodies utility,
style, grandeur and comfort, a rich blend of
landscape gardens and architecture. Join us
on an exciting journey as the estate
rejuvenates itself over the years and the
stories and histories that led to it being
described as a 'perfect paradise' are
uncovered. You can explore the sweeping
parkland, wander through a landscape
peppered with monuments and discover

the Park Farm, created at the cutting-edge of agricultural reforms. In the Georgian mansion, unearth prized treasures and experience life 'below stairs', then enter a world of glamour and royalty in the apartment of Patrick Lichfield, 5th Earl and fashion photographer.

Access: 🅿️ 🚻 ♿ ♿

Find out more: 01889 880160 or
shugborough@nationaltrust.org.uk
nationaltrust.org.uk/shugborough

Morning mist drifts over Shugborough Estate's park, below, and visitors explore the mansion, above

Sunnycroft

Wellington, near Telford, Shropshire

1999 🏠♿

Hidden down an avenue of towering redwoods is this 'estate in miniature' sitting in the middle of suburbia. This rare survival of a Victorian red-brick villa, glasshouses and garden was a much-loved family home. The wide lawn for games, pretty borders and orchard offer a haven to relax in. **Satnav**: use TF1 2DP (exit seven from M54).

Access: 🅿️♿♿♿♿

Find out more: 01952 242884 or sunnycroft@nationaltrust.org.uk 200 Holyhead Road, Wellington, near Telford, Shropshire TF1 2DR **nationaltrust.org.uk/sunnycroft**

Sunnycroft, Shropshire: an 'estate in miniature'

Upton House and Gardens

near Banbury, Warwickshire OX15 6HT

1948 🏠♿

Upton House and Gardens in Warwickshire

In 1927 Lord and Lady Bearsted extensively remodelled Upton House to create the perfect country residence for their family. Alongside spaces to showcase a world-class art and porcelain collection, including works by Bosch, Stubbs and El Greco, the gardens were altered to make the most of their position. Located on the edge of an ice-age valley, the gardens drop away from the south lawn down towards the Mirror Pool. They give you the opportunity to step away from busy lives as you meander past the borders, each of which has been planted to be at its seasonal best.

One of the many fascinating corners in Upton House

Note: steep paths and open water. **Satnav**: on arrival follow brown signs to car park.

Access: 🅿️ 🐕 📷 🚻 ♿

Find out more: 01295 670266 or uptonhouse@nationaltrust.org.uk **nationaltrust.org.uk/upton**

The Weir Garden

Swainshill, Hereford, Herefordshire HR4 7QF

1959 🏛️ ✿ ⛵

Whatever the season, the natural beauty of this riverside garden is completely captivating. During spring, the ground

beneath the ancient trees is carpeted with bulbs; then, in summer, a picnic by the river while watching the wildlife is irresistible. Autumn brings an abundance of seasonal produce in the walled garden. **Note**: sturdy footwear recommended.

Access: 🚻

Find out more: 01981 590509 or theweir@nationaltrust.org.uk **nationaltrust.org.uk/weir**

Wenlock Edge

Shropshire 1981

A ribbon of ancient woodland along a narrow limestone escarpment, with flower-rich grasslands, old quarries, lime kilns and far-reaching views. **Note**: some steep paths and steps. Nearest toilets in Much Wenlock. **Satnav**: use TF13 6AS for Much Wenlock car park and TF13 6DQ for Presthope car park.

Find out more: 01694 725000 or wenlockedge@nationaltrust.org.uk **nationaltrust.org.uk/wenlock-edge**

Wichenford Dovecote

Wichenford, Worcestershire WR6 6XY 1965

Small but striking 17th-century half-timbered dovecote at Wichenford Court. **Note**: no access to Wichenford Court (privately owned). Sorry no toilet.

Find out more: 01527 821214 or wichenforddovecote@nationaltrust.org.uk **nationaltrust.org.uk/wichenford-dovecote**

Wightwick Manor and Gardens

Bridgnorth Road, Wolverhampton,
West Midlands WV6 8BN

1937

A place where liberal dreams for the future mix with a love for unfashionable art. The Mander family's political ideals inspired them to share their home and fill it with art for the nation to enjoy. Their belief in social activism, the right to roam, fairness for their employees and confronting fascism combines with a home bursting with works by the greatest artists of the pre-Raphaelites and Arts and Crafts movement.

Wightwick Manor and Gardens, West Midlands

The liberal Manders family filled Wightwick Manor with art for everyone to enjoy

A house of colour and comfort; a garden of yew and roses; and a gallery of De Morgan treasures – the legacy of one remarkable family and their friends.

Access:

Find out more: 01902 761400 or
wightwickmanor@nationaltrust.org.uk
Wightwick Bank, Wolverhampton,
West Midlands WV6 8EE
nationaltrust.org.uk/wightwick-manor

Wilderhope Manor

Longville, Much Wenlock,
Shropshire TF13 6EG 1936

Charming Elizabethan manor house with commanding views across a secluded valley with many original features inside and lovely walks outside. **Note**: Youth Hostel, access may be restricted.

Find out more: 01694 771363 (Hostel Warden YHA) or
wilderhope@nationaltrust.org.uk
nationaltrust.org.uk/wilderhope-manor

North West

The Victorian-style garden at 500-year-old
Rufford Old Hall in Lancashire

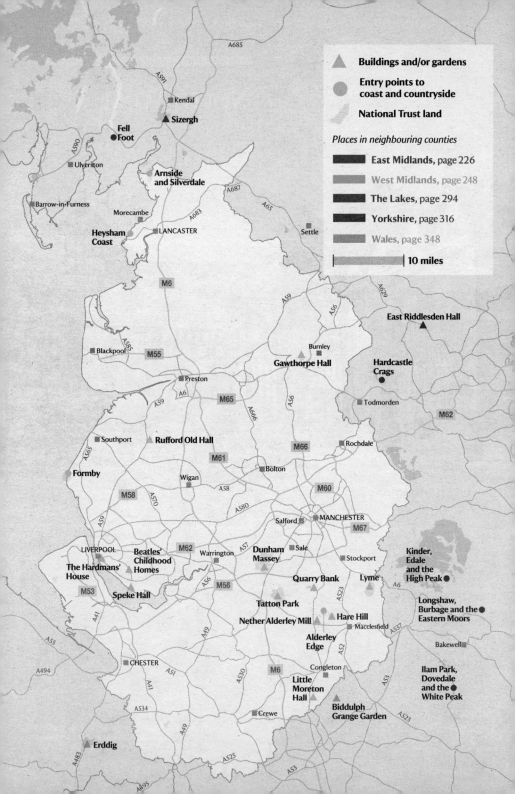

Places in neighbouring counties

East Midlands, page 226
West Midlands, page 248
The Lakes, page 294
Yorkshire, page 316
Wales, page 348

Buildings and/or gardens

Entry points to coast and countryside

National Trust land

10 miles

Kendal

Sizergh

Fell Foot

Ulverston

Arnside and Silverdale

Barrow-in-Furness

Morecambe

Heysham Coast

LANCASTER

Settle

M6

East Riddlesden Hall

Blackpool

Burnley

Gawthorpe Hall

Hardcastle Crags

M55

Preston

Todmorden

M62

M65

Southport

Rufford Old Hall

Rochdale

M66

Formby

M61

Wigan

Bolton

M58

M60

M6

A58

A580

Salford

MANCHESTER

M67

LIVERPOOL

Beatles' Childhood Homes

M62

Warrington

Dunham Massey

Sale

Stockport

Kinder, Edale and the High Peak

The Hardmans' House

Quarry Bank

Lyme

M53

Speke Hall

Longshaw, Burbage and the Eastern Moors

Tatton Park

Hare Hill

Nether Alderley Mill

Macclesfield

Bakewell

Alderley Edge

CHESTER

Congleton

M6

Little Moreton Hall

Ilam Park, Dovedale and the White Peak

Crewe

Biddulph Grange Garden

Erddig

Alderley Edge and Cheshire Countryside

Nether Alderley, near Macclesfield, Cheshire

Alderley Edge and Cheshire Countryside

The dramatic red sandstone escarpment of Alderley Edge has far-reaching views over the Cheshire Plain and towards the Peak District. There are plenty of paths to follow through open pasture and woodland. It's a Site of Special Scientific Interest because of its geology and history of copper mining dating back to the Bronze Age, and is also known for its wizard myth, which inspired the novel *The Weirdstone of Brisingamen*. There's more Cheshire countryside to explore: Bickerton, Bulkeley and Helsby Hills on the Sandstone Ridge, Thurstaston Common on the Wirral, and The Cloud and Mow Cop on the Staffordshire border.
Note: toilets at Alderley Edge car park only.
Satnav: use SK10 4UB for Alderley Edge; ST7 3PA for Mow Cop; SY14 8LN for Bickerton.

Access:

Find out more: 01625 584412 or alderleyedge@nationaltrust.org.uk
nationaltrust.org.uk/alderley-edge

Arnside and Silverdale

near Arnside, Cumbria

1929

This wildlife-rich coastal landscape of grassland, woodland, meadows and rugged limestone pavement has miles of footpaths to explore, with views over Morecambe Bay. Arnside Knott and Eaves Wood are home to butterflies and wild flowers, while Jack Scout's cliffs are perfect for watching the sunset or spotting passing migrant birds.
Satnav: use LA5 0BP for Arnside Knott; LA5 0UG for Eaves Wood (Silverdale), both nearby.

Find out more: 01524 701178 or arnsidesilverdale@nationaltrust.org.uk
nationaltrust.org.uk/arnside-and-silverdale

Looking out over Morecambe Bay from wildlife-rich Arnside and Silverdale, Cumbria

The Beatles' Childhood Homes

Woolton and Allerton, Liverpool

2002

Explore Mendips and 20 Forthlin Road, the childhood homes of John Lennon and Paul McCartney and where The Beatles met, composed and rehearsed many of their earliest songs. You can walk through the back door into the kitchen and imagine John's Aunt Mimi cooking him his tea, or stand in the spot where Lennon and McCartney composed 'I Saw Her Standing There'. This is the opportunity to take a fascinating trip down memory lane in these two atmospheric houses, so typical of Liverpool life in the 1950s. **Note**: handbags, cameras and recording equipment must be left in secure facilities at both houses.

The Beatles' Childhood Homes, Liverpool, above and below: from such modest beginnings sprang musical genius

Access:

Find out more: 0151 427 7231 (Speke Hall) or thebeatleshomes@nationaltrust.org.uk **nationaltrust.org.uk/beatles**

Dunham Massey

Altrincham, Greater Manchester WA14 4SJ

1976

Tucked away south of urban Manchester, Dunham Massey is a green haven – a place to meet, walk and escape. You can take a gentle stroll through the deer park and gardens, home to wildlife and ancient trees. Among the seasonal highlights in the gardens are snowdrops, bluebells, tulips, roses and one of the largest winter gardens in the UK. Explore inside the house for stories and collections amassed over 300 years, and discover the working water-powered mill and servants' courtyard. The surrounding canals and footpaths make exploring the 1,200 hectares (3,000 acres) of rolling farmland easy all year round.

Dunham Massey, Greater Manchester: a place to walk and escape

It is hard to believe that Dunham Massey sits tucked away just south of the hustle and bustle of urban Manchester

Note: everyone requires a house and/or garden ticket, including members (available from reception on the day).

Access: ♿♿♿♿♿♿♿

Find out more: 0161 942 3989 (Infoline). 0161 941 1025 or dunhammassey@nationaltrust.org.uk
nationaltrust.org.uk/dunham-massey

Formby

near Formby, Liverpool

1967 🏛🏖🎨🦮

As well as 3 miles of shifting sands and dynamic dunes, Formby offers scenic views over Liverpool Bay to the hills of North Wales. Along the shore, you might see footprint trails that are more than 5,000 years old reappearing as the sea erodes the ancient mudflats. In the sweeping pinewoods surrounding the beach, you can take a walk and spot red squirrels, or follow the Asparagus Trail to discover the local heritage of this vegetable. The beach at Lifeboat Road is supervised by lifeguards during summer weekends and holidays, making it the perfect setting for family days out.

Formby: perfect sand for building sandcastles

Note: toilets open when car parks are staffed. **Satnav**: use L37 1LJ for Victoria Road car park; L37 2EB for Lifeboat Road.

Access: 🅿♿🚻♿

Find out more: 01704 878591 or formby@nationaltrust.org.uk
nationaltrust.org.uk/formby

Formby, Liverpool: a place of shifting sands, scenic views and dynamic dunes

Gawthorpe Hall

near Burnley, Lancashire

1972 🏠🌀⚓

Gawthorpe Hall in Lancashire offers extravagant 19th-century interiors and wonderful treasures

This Elizabethan house, in the heart of urban Lancashire, has extravagant 19th-century interiors by Sir Charles Barry (known for his role in rebuilding the Houses of Parliament). The Hall displays textiles from the Gawthorpe Textile Collection, including needlework, lace and embroidery. Outside, you can enjoy the garden and woodland walks. **Note**: cared for in partnership with Lancashire County Council. **Satnav**: use BB12 8SD then follow brown signs.

Access: 🚶♿

Find out more: 01282 771004 or gawthorpehall@nationaltrust.org.uk
Burnley Road, Padiham, near Burnley, Lancashire BB12 8UA
nationaltrust.org.uk/gawthorpe

The Hardmans' House

59 Rodney Street, Liverpool, Merseyside L1 9ER

2003 🏠

Discover Liverpool's best-kept secret and step inside a true time capsule – the home and studio of a 1950s society photographer. The handsome Georgian house, both glamorous workplace and modest home for Edward Chambré Hardman and his talented wife Margaret, is packed with vintage treasures and fascinating photography. **Note**: entrance on Pilgrim Street at rear of property.

Access: 🚶♿🅿

Find out more: 0151 709 6261 or thehardmanshouse@nationaltrust.org.uk
nationaltrust.org.uk/hardmans

Hare Hill

Over Alderley, Macclesfield,
Cheshire SK10 4PY

1978

Hare Hill (above), is a place to refresh the senses as well as the soul. Surrounded by farmland, this wooded garden is full of twists, turns and surprises, hidden paths and ponds. At its heart is the walled garden with its white flowering borders, which offers an oasis of tranquillity. **Satnav**: postcode takes you 109 yards west of car park.

Access:

Find out more: 01625 827534 or
harehill@nationaltrust.org.uk
nationaltrust.org.uk/hare-hill

Heysham Coast

Heysham, near Morecambe,
Lancashire 1996

A sandstone headland with a scenic walk through grassland and woodland, passing a ruined Saxon chapel and unusual rock-cut graves. **Note**: nearest facilities in village (not National Trust); park in the main village car park. **Satnav**: use LA3 2RW.

Find out more: 01524 701178 or
heysham@nationaltrust.org.uk
nationaltrust.org.uk/heysham-coast

Little Moreton Hall

Congleton, Cheshire CW12 4SD

1938

As you cross the moat into this Tudor fantasy you leave the chaos of modern life behind. Built to impress by craftsmen more than 500 years ago, the Hall has a unique quirky charm and homely feel. With its crooked walls and uneven floors, it seems so resilient yet still so fragile. Outside there's a manicured knot garden and borders with herbs and vegetables used by the Tudors. You can step back in time and

Leave the chaos of modern life behind and enter a Tudor fantasy at quirky Little Moreton Hall in Cheshire

Let off steam, above, and learn about the Tudors' favourite herbs, below, in the garden at Little Moreton Hall

reflect on the ups and downs of a simpler way of life at Little Moreton Hall, a remarkable survivor with an inspiring story to tell.

Access: 🅿️ 🅳 ♿ 🚻 ♿

Find out more: 01260 272018 or littlemoretonhall@nationaltrust.org.uk
nationaltrust.org.uk/little-moreton-hall

Lyme

Disley, Stockport, Cheshire SK12 2NR

1947 🏠 ➕ 💧 🏊

If you imagine a classic English country house, you're probably picturing somewhere just like Lyme. The house sits in 570 hectares (1,400 acres) of moorland and deer park, with views across Manchester and Cheshire. Home to the Legh family for over 550 years, the interiors tell the story of centuries of change up to and beyond its Regency heyday, when Thomas Legh created the house and garden you see today.

You may recognise Lyme as 'Pemberley' from the BBC's *Pride and Prejudice*, starring Colin Firth. Lyme's ever-changing gardens, with the Reflection Lake, Orangery and Rose Garden, are an ideal place to unwind. Explore the diverse scenery of the park on its many footpaths, including links to the Gritstone Trail.

Access: 🅿️ 🅳 ♿ 🚻 ♿

Find out more: 01663 762023 or lyme@nationaltrust.org.uk
nationaltrust.org.uk/lyme

Lyme in Cheshire, below and right, is the epitome of a classic English country house

Nether Alderley Mill

Congleton Road, Nether Alderley, Macclesfield, Cheshire SK10 4TW

1950

Nether Alderley Mill, Cheshire, is a fully restored, water-powered, working corn mill

Hidden under the long sloping roof of this medieval building is a fully restored, working corn mill. Learn about the life of a miller and spot centuries-old graffiti, then watch the waterwheels turn, powering the huge millstones that grind the flour.
Note: uneven floor, steep stairs and low ceilings. Sorry no toilet/catering.

Access:

Find out more: 01625 527468 or netheralderleymill@nationaltrust.org.uk
nationaltrust.org.uk/nether-alderley-mill

Quarry Bank

Styal, Wilmslow, Cheshire SK9 4LA

1939

Standing in the gardens, you can almost feel the tranquillity of the river valley giving way to the clatter and bustle of a giant cotton mill as it led the way into the Industrial Revolution. The people here lived during a time of great change, from the mill-owning Greg family in Quarry Bank House, to the workers living in Styal village and the Apprentice House. Discover what life was like for the men, women and children toiling long hours in the heat of the mill, where you can still see working historic machinery in action. The very different lives led by the mill owners becomes apparent when you walk through their estate, picturesque gardens and elegant family home.

Access:

Find out more: 01625 527468 or quarrybank@nationaltrust.org.uk
nationaltrust.org.uk/quarry-bank

Quarry Bank, Cheshire: inside the giant cotton mill

The valley setting of Quarry Bank's peaceful gardens give way to views of the adjoining mill, a powerhouse of the Industrial Revolution

Ruford Old Hall in Lancashire

Rufford Old Hall

200 Liverpool Road, Rufford, near Ormskirk, Lancashire L40 1SG

1936

This black-and-white Tudor building, with its contrasting mellow red-brick Jacobean wing, hunkers in the low-lying mosslands of south-west Lancashire. More than 500 years old, this family home has many stories to tell about the intriguing people who used to live here, as well as a Great Hall that might make your jaw drop! Children can get closer to nature with bug-hunting and wild art kits, and you can unwind in the Victorian-style garden and grounds, with their colourful seasonal displays – from carpets of bluebells in spring, to golden leaves in autumn.

Access:

Find out more: 01704 821254 or rufforfoldhall@nationaltrust.org.uk
nationaltrust.org.uk/rufford-old-hall

Tatton Park

Knutsford, Cheshire

1960 ⟦icons⟧

Tatton Park is a grand country estate set in 400 hectares (1,000 acres) of historic deer park. The Egerton family acquired an impressive collection of paintings, books and rich furnishings, which can be seen in the 18th-century mansion – which also houses the servants' quarters. There is a medieval Old Hall and 20 hectares (50 acres) of award-winning gardens, including the 100-year-old Japanese Garden.

There is so much to see and do at Tatton Park, Cheshire, as these three very different views show

The working farm and restored agricultural mill tell the story of Tatton's food production over the centuries, and you can see original machinery in action and meet rare breed animals and characters from the past. **Note**: financed and managed by Cheshire East Council. **Satnav**: use WA16 6SG.

Access: ⟦icons⟧

Find out more: 01625 374400 or tatton@cheshireeast.gov.uk
Knutsford, Cheshire WA16 6QN
nationaltrust.org.uk/tatton-park
tattonpark.org.uk

Approaching storm clouds are not enough to dampen spirits at Tarn Hows in Cumbria

The Lakes

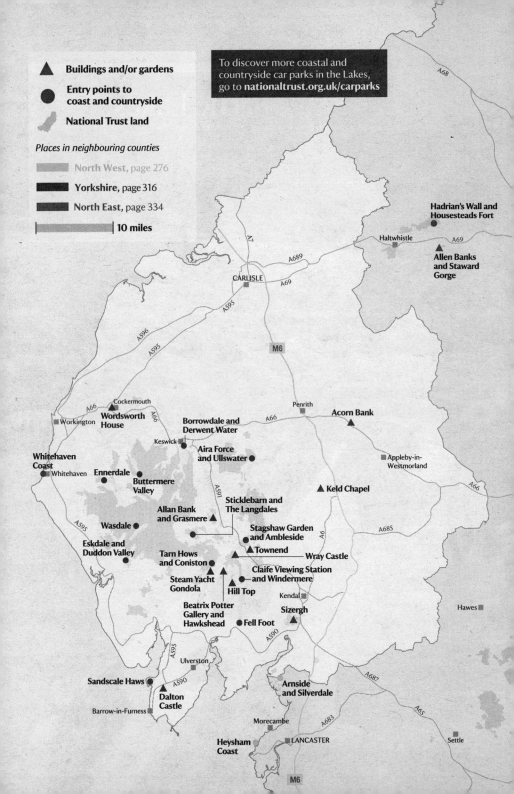

To discover more coastal and countryside car parks in the Lakes, go to **nationaltrust.org.uk/carparks**

Buildings and/or gardens

Entry points to coast and countryside

National Trust land

Places in neighbouring counties

North West, page 276

Yorkshire, page 316

North East, page 334

10 miles

Hadrian's Wall and Housesteads Fort

Haltwhistle

Allen Banks and Staward Gorge

CARLISLE

A68

A69

A689

A595

A596

A595

M6

Cockermouth

Wordsworth House

Workington

Penrith

A66

Acorn Bank

Borrowdale and Derwent Water

Keswick

Aira Force and Ullswater

Appleby-in-Westmorland

Whitehaven Coast

Whitehaven

Ennerdale

Buttermere Valley

Keld Chapel

A66

Allan Bank and Grasmere

Sticklebarn and The Langdales

Wasdale

Stagshaw Garden and Ambleside

A591

Eskdale and Duddon Valley

Tarn Hows and Coniston

Townend

Wray Castle

A595

Steam Yacht Gondola

Claife Viewing Station and Windermere

A6

A685

Beatrix Potter Gallery and Hawkshead

Hill Top

Kendal

Sizergh

Hawes

Fell Foot

Ulverston

A590

Sandscale Haws

Dalton Castle

Barrow-in-Furness

A687

Arnside and Silverdale

A683

A65

Morecambe

Heysham Coast

LANCASTER

Settle

M6

Acorn Bank

Temple Sowerby, near Penrith,
Cumbria CA10 1SP

1950

Close to Penrith and with views to the Lake District and Howgill Fells, Acorn Bank is a tranquil haven in the heart of the Eden Valley. Established by the Knights Templar around the 13th century; people have lived and worked here for more than 800 years. Today the walled gardens shelter a medicinal herb garden, herbaceous borders, lily-filled pond and traditional orchards carpeted with spring daffodils. Woodland walks reveal a half-hidden story of gypsum mining, working medieval watermill and a wildlife-rich estate.

Note: the 17th-century manor is closed. Some paths may be closed following wet weather.

Access:

Find out more:
acornbank@nationaltrust.org.uk
nationaltrust.org.uk/acorn-bank

Acorn Bank in Cumbria, above and this picture; find tranquillity in the garden

Aira Force and Ullswater, Cumbria: a place of contrasts, with wild open countryside, this picture, and thundering waterfalls, below

Aira Force and Ullswater

near Watermillock, Penrith, Cumbria

1906 🖫

An 18th-century pleasure ground, Aira Force was the backdrop for William Wordsworth's poem 'Somnambulist' – a Gothic tale of love and tragedy. There are so many woodland trails to discover in this landscape of contrasts. Quiet glades give way to dramatic waterfalls, with Aira Beck thundering down a 65-foot drop past ferns and rocks. If you walk to the summit of Gowbarrow, you will be rewarded with panoramic views over Ullswater. Starting

your day in Glenridding, arriving at Aira Force by boat, then strolling back along the lakeshore, allows you to take in the wonderful Ullswater Valley sights.
Note: boat rides on Ullswater operated by Ullswater 'Steamers', not National Trust.
Satnav: use CA11 0JS for Aira Force; CA11 0NQ for Glencoyne Bay.

Access: 🅿️♿ 🚻♿

Find out more: 017684 82067 or ullswater@nationaltrust.org.uk
nationaltrust.org.uk/aira-force

Allan Bank and Grasmere

near Ambleside, Cumbria

1920 🏠🏛️✿🖫

Views of Grasmere lake and the surrounding fells can be enjoyed from the large bay windows and woodland grounds of this relaxed house. Once home to National Trust co-founder Canon Rawnsley, Allan Bank is now only partially decorated. Red squirrels play in the grounds, there are picnic spots indoors and out, places for children to run free and you can even sit by the fire and read a book. Lakeshore strolls

Allan Bank and Grasmere, Cumbria

Beatrix Potter Gallery and Hawkshead

Main Street, Hawkshead,
Cumbria LA22 0NS

1947

Take in changing exhibitions of Beatrix Potter's original artwork, illustrations and letters, within the 17th-century building which once served as the office of Beatrix's solicitor husband. Each year discover new stories about this inspiring woman and her life. If you've ever been charmed by Beatrix's endearing characters, you can take a closer look at some of her miniature masterpieces in a rare opportunity to see the delicate watercolours that are shown only once a decade. Quaint Hawkshead

Beatrix Potter Gallery and Hawkshead, Cumbria: the charming Gallery

Picture-perfect view from Allan Bank

and adventurous fell-top rambles can be started from nearby Grasmere village.
Note: follow directions on foot from The Inn at Grasmere.
Satnav: use LA22 9TA for nearest car park.

Access:

Find out more: 015394 35143 or allanbank@nationaltrust.org.uk near Ambleside, Cumbria LA22 9QB
nationaltrust.org.uk/allan-bank

Borrowdale and Derwent Water

near Keswick, Cumbria

1902

From the lakeshore at Crow Park, a few minutes' walk from the centre of the busy Lakeland town of Keswick, there are far-reaching views across Derwent Water and its islands to the high central fells, framed by Cat Bells and Walla Crag. Castle Crag sits between the lake and upper Borrowdale, where scenic drives, traditional hamlets and waymarked walks await. Nine car parks in the valley make it easy to access some of Lakeland's most photographed views and walks. During the summer Seatoller and Bowder Stone offer the best chance of a parking spot.

Snow-capped hills beyond Borrowdale and Derwent Water in Cumbria

Quaint Hawkshead, top, and the Beatrix Potter Gallery, above

village makes the perfect base for exploring the countryside that inspired Beatrix and many other famous poets, writers and artists. **Note**: nearest toilets 300 yards in main village car park (not National Trust).

Access:

Find out more: 015394 36355 (gallery) or beatrixpottergallery@nationaltrust.org.uk
nationaltrust.org.uk/beatrix-potter-gallery

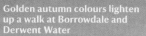
Golden autumn colours lighten up a walk at Borrowdale and Derwent Water

Cycling at Borrowdale and Derwent Water

October brings rich auburns and golden evening light to Ashness Bridge and Surprise View, and from Kettlewell the autumn colours are reflected in the lake. **Satnav**: use CA12 5UP for Great Wood car park.

Access: 🚻♿

Find out more: 017687 74649 or borrowdale@nationaltrust.org.uk
nationaltrust.org.uk/borrowdale

Buttermere Valley

near Cockermouth, Cumbria

| 1935 |

Peaceful Buttermere Valley in Cumbria also offers drama

This dramatic valley encompasses the lakes of Buttermere, Crummock Water and Loweswater, all offering easy low-level lakeshore walks and access onto the high fells. Buttermere's 4½-mile round-the-lake path takes in shingle beaches, cascading waterfalls and a hand-cut Victorian tunnel, perfect for family adventures. Top tip: arrive early to get parking. **Note**: toilets at Buttermere village only (not National Trust). **Satnav**: use CA13 9UZ for Buttermere; CA13 0RT for Crummock Water; CA13 0RU for Loweswater.

Find out more: 017687 74649 or buttermere@nationaltrust.org.uk
nationaltrust.org.uk/buttermere

Wonderful walking in Buttermere Valley

Claife Viewing Station and Windermere West Shore

near Far Sawrey, Cumbria LA22 0LW

| 1962 |

Perched on the tranquil west shore of Windermere, minutes from the Bowness ferry, Claife Viewing Station was built in the 1790s for the first tourists to the Lake District. Today, you can enjoy the same panoramic views of the lake from the platform, framed by coloured glass. At the café you can sit by a cosy fire or under the fairy lights that welcome you into the courtyard. There are 4 miles of lakeside paths leading towards Wray Castle for cycling or walking, or you could explore the landscape around Hill Top and Hawkshead that so inspired Beatrix Potter.

Claife Viewing Station and Windermere West Shore in Cumbria: the colourful 1790s Viewing Station

The Viewing Station boasts panoramic lake views

Note: toilets at nearby Ferry House. Passenger boats operated by Windermere Lake Cruises; car ferry council-run. **Satnav**: use LA22 0LP for Ash Landing; LA22 0LR for Harrowslack; LA22 0JH for Red Nab (all nearby).

Access: 🅿🕭

Find out more: 015394 41456 or claife@nationaltrust.org.uk
nationaltrust.org.uk/claife-viewing-station

Dalton Castle

Market Place, Dalton-in-Furness, Cumbria LA15 8AX 1965

Standing proud in Dalton town centre, this impressive 14th-century tower was once the manorial courthouse of Furness Abbey. **Note**: opened on behalf of the National Trust by the Friends of Dalton Castle.

Find out more: 015395 69816 or daltoncastle@nationaltrust.org.uk
nationaltrust.org.uk/dalton-castle

Ennerdale

Bowness Knott, Croasdale, Ennerdale Bridge, Cumbria

1927 🏛🕭

Peaceful, yet dramatic, Ennerdale is home to one of the UK's largest wildland partnerships – Wild Ennerdale. A horseshoe of rugged fells surrounds the wooded valley where Galloway cattle roam free and the untamed River Liza flows. The views widen across Ennerdale Water, which is circled by lakeshore paths and beaches. **Note**: sorry no toilet. **Satnav**: CA23 3AU for Bowness Knott; CA23 3AS for Bleach Green.

Find out more: 017687 74649 or ennerdale@nationaltrust.org.uk
nationaltrust.org.uk/ennerdale

Ennerdale, Cumbria, offers rugged fells, wild woods, beaches and tempting paths

Eskdale and Duddon Valley

Eskdale, near Ravenglass; Duddon Valley, near Broughton in Furness, Cumbria

1926 🏠♿🐾

Eskdale is a valley of contrasts. Upper Eskdale leads to the high mountains, including Scafell and Bowfell; the valley floor has meandering riverside and woodland paths, including the Eskdale Trail, for walkers and cyclists. Across high mountain passes lies the Duddon Valley, with meadows, woodlands, mountains, hill farms and rivers.

Find out more: 019467 26064 or eskdaleandduddon@nationaltrust.org.uk
nationaltrust.org.uk/eskdale

Cyclists explore Eskdale and Duddon Valley, Cumbria

Fell Foot

Newby Bridge, Windermere, Cumbria

1948 🏠♿

A young sailor at Fell Foot in Cumbria

Less than a 20-minute drive from the M6 at the most southern end of Windermere, Fell Foot is one of the few places where you can access England's largest lake. This family-friendly park is perfect for paddling, boat hire or swimming, whether you're experienced or a beginner, and state-of-the-art changing facilities at the Active Base offer a comfortable place to dry off after a day on the water. If you'd rather stay on land, relax on the lawn for a summer picnic with impressive mountain views, or stroll along the paths to the meadow and Pinetum – the park's collection of specimen trees. Three recently restored Gothic Revival boathouses uncover the park's rich history. **Note**: additional charges (including members) for launch facilities, rowing boats, paddleboards and kayaks. Also for Active Base (pass needed – available from shop). **Satnav**: use LA12 8NN.

Access: 🅿️ 🅳 🐾 🎣

Find out more: 015395 31273 or fellfoot@nationaltrust.org.uk
nationaltrust.org.uk/fell-foot

Picnic with a view at Fell Foot

Beatrix Potter's much-loved farmhouse, Hill Top in Cumbria, above and below, remains much as she left it

Hill Top

Near Sawrey, Hawkshead, Ambleside, Cumbria LA22 0LF

1944 🏠 ❖

Beatrix Potter's beloved farmhouse Hill Top was her sanctuary and a source of inspiration for her much-loved children's tales. Near Sawrey village and Beatrix's garden path are home to landmarks and scenes from her illustrations. Filled with her personal possessions, including Lakeland furniture and trophies for her prize-winning Herdwick sheep, the house is a true

Check opening dates and times before you set out: nationaltrust.org.uk

reminder of Beatrix's legacy. It remains much as she left it when it came into the Trust's care in 1944. The surrounding landscape is great for exploring – it inspired Beatrix to gift 14 farms and 1,618 hectares (4,000 acres) to the National Trust.

Access: 🅿️♿

Find out more: 015394 36269 or hilltop@nationaltrust.org.uk
nationaltrust.org.uk/hill-top

Keld Chapel

Keld Lane, Shap,
Cumbria CA10 3NW ⟨1918⟩

Tucked away in east Cumbria, this rustic 16th-century stone chapel was once the chantry for Shap Abbey.
Note: sorry no facilities.
Satnav: use CA10 3NW.

Find out more: 017683 61893 or keldchapel@nationaltrust.org.uk
nationaltrust.org.uk/keld-chapel

Sandscale Haws National Nature Reserve

near Barrow-in-Furness,
Cumbria ⟨1984⟩

This beach has wild, grass-covered dunes and Lakeland mountain views; it's the perfect habitat for rare wildlife, including natterjack toads. **Satnav:** use LA14 4QJ.

Find out more: 015395 60951 or sandscalehaws@nationaltrust.org.uk
nationaltrust.org.uk/sandscale-haws

Sizergh

Sizergh, near Kendal, Cumbria LA8 8DZ

⟨1950⟩ 🏛️🏚️❀♿

Standing proud at the gateway to the National Park, this imposing medieval manor is home to the Strickland family and a great place to stop on your way in or out of the Lake District. Built more than 650 years ago and filled with thousands of items collected by 26 generations of the family, the jewel in Sizergh's crown is the elaborate wooden panelling in the Inlaid Chamber, one of the best examples of Elizabethan craftsmanship in the world.

Medieval Sizergh in Cumbria stands proud at the gateway to the Lake District National Park

The 647-hectare (1,600-acre) estate contains wetlands, woodlands and orchards and is home to fritillary butterflies, deer and elusive hawfinches. There's somewhere to relax in the garden whatever the season, with an apple orchard, herbaceous border, fruit wall and rock garden. **Satnav**: use LA8 8DZ – takes you to the Strickland Arms, then follow National Trust signs.

Access: 🅿️ 🐕 ♿ 🚻 ♿ ♿

Find out more: 015395 60951 or sizergh@nationaltrust.org.uk **nationaltrust.org.uk/sizergh**

Imposing Sizergh sits within an extensive estate

Sizergh boasts many treasures, including unrivalled Elizabethan craftsmanship

Stagshaw Garden and Ambleside

near Windermere, Cumbria

1927

Perched above Ambleside, this quiet, informal woodland garden is hidden from the hustle and bustle of the town below. Rambling paths and unusual combinations of shrubs, trees and plants give an enchanted feel. In spring it becomes a kaleidoscope of colour with daffodils, bluebells, azaleas and rhododendrons in full bloom. **Note**: Ambleside Roman Fort is owned by the National Trust and managed by English Heritage. **Satnav**: use LA22 0HE for Stagshaw Garden and Skelghyll Woods; LA22 9AN for Bridge House.

Find out more: 015394 46402 or stagshawgarden@nationaltrust.org.uk **nationaltrust.org.uk/ambleside**

Stagshaw Garden and Ambleside, Cumbria: informal and enchanting

Steam Yacht Gondola

Coniston Pier, Lake Road, Coniston, Cumbria LA21 8AN

1980

Steam Yacht Gondola powers across Coniston Water in Cumbria, with Coniston Fells as a backdrop

A steam-powered yacht on Coniston Water, Gondola was rebuilt by the National Trust based on the original 1859 version. With inspiration taken from a traditional Venetian 'Burchiello' boat, Steam Yacht Gondola features the carved figurehead of Sid the Golden Sea Serpent at the bow of her streamlined hull and an elegant cabin with two indoor saloons. The Coniston Fells provide an impressive backdrop to your cruise, with opportunities to alight at jetties around the lake. As you pass famous

Sticklebarn and The Langdales

near Ambleside, Cumbria

1925 🏛️🔧

A striking U-shaped valley, Langdale was described by the leading English art critic John Ruskin as 'the loveliest rock scenery, chased with silver waterfalls that I have ever set foot or heart upon'. This outdoor playground offers miles of walking, cycling and climbing routes, from a high-level scramble on the Langdale Pikes to a low-level stroll around Blea Tarn. Below the peaks sits Sticklebarn, a National Trust-run pub serving food and drink that celebrate Cumbria's food heritage and local produce.

Steam Yacht Gondola: a day out on the water is guaranteed to bring joy to visitors of all ages

landmarks, the crew provide a commentary on Gondola's history on the lake and association with the famous *Swallows and Amazons*. **Note**: cruises depart from Coniston Pier (subject to weather). Sorry no toilet on scheduled sailings. Steam Yacht Gondola (a member of National Historic Ships Fleet) is very costly to run.

Access: 🅿️🖼️📶

Find out more: 015394 32733 or sygondola@nationaltrust.org.uk
nationaltrust.org.uk/gondola

A scenic camping pitch at Sticklebarn and The Langdales, Cumbria

Serious hiking, top, and celebratory drinking, above, at Sticklebarn and The Langdales

An outdoor terrace and open fires offer the perfect place to share stories of adventures on the fells over a pint of Cumbrian ale. **Satnav:** use LA22 9JU for Sticklebarn; LA22 9PG for Blea Tarn; LA22 9HP for Elterwater; LA22 9HJ for High Close Estate.

Access: 🅿️♿ 🚻 ♪

Find out more: 015394 37356 (Sticklebarn) or sticklebarn@nationaltrust.org.uk
nationaltrust.org.uk/sticklebarn

Tarn Hows and Coniston

near Coniston, Cumbria

1930

An accessible walk for all the family whatever the weather, Tarn Hows showcases ever-changing scenery and views of the high fells. The circular 1¾-mile path through a 19th-century man-made landscape makes it a favourite with walkers of all abilities. Arrive early or late for a meditative moment with mountain views. **Note**: toilets in main car park. Mobility scooters free to hire (donations welcome). Livestock grazing. **Satnav**: does not work, instead follow signs from B5285, Coniston or Hawkshead Hill.

Access:

Find out more: 015394 41456 or tarnhows@nationaltrust.org.uk
nationaltrust.org.uk/tarn-hows

Townend

Troutbeck, Windermere, Cumbria LA23 1LB

1948

A cosy farmhouse (below left) near Windermere brimming with character. Home to the Browne family for 400 years, Townend is full of intricately carved furniture and rare books, including 44 that are the only remaining copies in the world. Warm yourself by the open fire and spend time in the cottage garden.

Access:

Find out more: 015394 32628 or townend@nationaltrust.org.uk
nationaltrust.org.uk/townend

Wasdale

near Gosforth, Cumbria

1920

Wasdale sits below some of England's highest mountains. From the tops of Illgill Head and Whin Rigg the screes sweep down, creating ever-changing reflections in Wastwater below. Great Gable stands at the head of the valley with Scafell Pike nearby. This is a remote mountain landscape for hill-walking, climbing and exploring.

Wasdale, Cumbria: the gentler aspect of the valley

Walkers on Scafell Pike in Wasdale, Cumbria

Towards the southern end of the lake and Nether Wasdale, winding paths weave through woodland and along the water's edge, revealing a gentler aspect to the valley. Planning ahead will give you the best experience: remember to check the weather forecast, prepare well and enjoy your day. **Satnav**: use CA20 1EX.

Find out more: 019467 26064 or wasdale@nationaltrust.org.uk
nationaltrust.org.uk/wasdale

Whitehaven Coast

Whitehaven, Cumbria 2008

Coast with a proud mining past. Enjoy bracing clifftop walks to St Bees Head from the sandstone Georgian harbour. **Note**: sorry no toilet. **Satnav**: use CA28 9BG for clifftop car park and CA28 7LY for Whitehaven Harbour.

Find out more: 017687 74649 or whitehavencoast@nationaltrust.org.uk
nationaltrust.org.uk/whitehaven-coast

Wordsworth House and Garden

Main Street, Cockermouth, Cumbria CA13 9RX

1938

Wordsworth House and Garden in Cumbria: an enduring love of nature and a lifetime of creativity began here

Wandering among the heritage fruit trees, flowers and vegetables of William Wordsworth's garden as the River Derwent gurgles by, it's easy to picture the wild child born here more than 250 years ago and imagine how his childhood home inspired a love of nature and a lifetime of creativity. Indoors, hands-on rooms, animations and audio offer a window into the Georgian world. Some days you may even spot

Wray Castle

Low Wray, Ambleside, Cumbria LA22 0JA

1929

In the 1840s a surgeon and an heiress from Liverpool began building a castle with panoramic Lake District views that would only ever have to defend itself from the Cumbrian weather. Last inhabited in the 1920s, and with the furniture and artwork long gone, the castle has had mixed use and first opened to visitors in 2011. A work in progress, we are continually learning more about the castle's history. Indoors, the ground floor is open to discover the church-like rooms. Outdoors, with the castle's turrets and towers providing the atmosphere, explore the grounds and enjoy walks along the shore of Windermere. **Note**: steep walk from jetty if arriving by boat.

Access:

Find out more: 015394 33250 or wraycastle@nationaltrust.org.uk
nationaltrust.org.uk/wray-castle

Wray Castle, Cumbria, boasts panoramic views

Wild times in the garden, top, and baking in the kitchen, above, at Wordsworth House and Garden

costumed servants cooking in the kitchen, while they gossip and tell tales.

Access:

Find out more: 01900 820884 (Infoline). 01900 824805 or wordsworthhouse@nationaltrust.org.uk
nationaltrust.org.uk/wordsworth-house

Built to only ever have to defend itself against the weather, Wray Castle, offers a wonderful day out

Yorkshire

The Rotunda at Wentworth Castle Gardens:
South Yorkshire's only Grade I-listed landscape

MIDDLESBROUGH ■ **Ormesby Hall** ▲

■ Darlington

Barnard
Castle ■

● **Roseberry Topping**

Stokesley ■

Whitby ■

Richmond ■

▲ **Mount Grace Priory**

■ Northallerton

**Bridestones,
Crosscliff
and Blakey
Topping** ●

● **Yorkshire Coast**

▲ **Braithwaite Hall**

**Rievaulx
Terrace** ▲

Scarborough ■

Thirsk ■

Pickering ■

A170

Filey ■

A168

▲ **Nunnington Hall**

● **Yorkshire Dales**

■ Ripon

A64

Bridlington ■

Settle ■

▲ **Fountains Abbey**

● **Brimham
Rocks**

▲ **Beningbrough Hall**

A166

Harrogate ■

Treasurer's House ▲

Skipton ■

Goddards House ▲ **YORK**

Wetherby ■

■ Beverley

**Middlethorpe
Hall**

East Riddlesden Hall
Keighley ■ ▲

Burnley ■

**Hardcastle
Crags** ▲

Bradford ■

Leeds ■

A63

Selby ■

M62

A64

Maister House
▲ Kingston upon Hull

Halifax ■

M621

M62

Pontefract ■

Rochdale ■

Huddersfield ■

Wakefield ■

▲ **Nostell**

M18

● **Marsden Moor**

M62

M1

BARNSLEY

M180

M60

**Wentworth
Castle Gardens** ▲

Doncaster ■

A635

**Kinder,
Edale
and the
Dark Peak** ●

A629

▲ **Wentworth
Woodhouse**

M18

A1(M)

Lyme ■

□ SHEFFIELD

A631

● **Longshaw,
Burbage and the
Eastern Moors**

Worksop ■

M6

▲ **Clumber Park**

▲ **Hardwick**

M1

▲ **Buildings and/or gardens**

● **Entry points to
coast and countryside**

National Trust land

H **Historic House Hotel**

Places in neighbouring counties

East Midlands, page 226

North West, page 276

├────┤ **10 miles**

Beningbrough Hall, Gallery and Gardens

Beningbrough, York,
North Yorkshire YO30 1DD

 1958

Two sunny views of Beningbrough Hall, Gallery and Gardens in North Yorkshire

The view of the Hall, surrounded by parkland, as you turn onto the long drive evokes images of an intriguing past. From the wealthy teenager who inherited it, to its time as an RAF billet, Beningbrough has been shaped for more than 300 years by the people who lived here. The spacious, light-filled Saloon Galleries display contemporary and historic art exhibitions. In the garden, the award-winning designer Andy Sturgeon's ha-ha walk and pergola contrast with the traditional herbaceous borders, sweeping lawns, walled and American gardens.

Access: 🅿️♿🏛️🚻♿♿

Find out more: 01904 472027 or beningbrough@nationaltrust.org.uk
nationaltrust.org.uk/beningbrough-hall

Braithwaite Hall

East Witton, Leyburn,
North Yorkshire DL8 4SY 1941

Grand 17th-century tenanted farmhouse in the heart of Coverdale, close to the River Cover and surrounded by farmland and woodland. **Note**: sorry, no toilet.

Find out more: 01969 640287 or braithwaitehall@nationaltrust.org.uk
nationaltrust.org.uk/braithwaite-hall

Bridestones, Crosscliff and Blakey Topping

near Pickering, North Yorkshire 1944

On the North York Moors, the Bridestones are geological wonders – rock formations with moorland views, woodland walks and grassy valleys. **Note**: nearest toilets at Staindale Lake car park. Road access is via Dalby Forest Drive starting 2½ miles north of Thornton le Dale: toll charges payable (including members) to Forestry England. **Satnav**: use YO18 7LR.

Find out more: 0191 529 3161 or bridestones@nationaltrust.org.uk
nationaltrust.org.uk/bridestones

Brimham Rocks, North Yorkshire: millions of years of wind and ice created the strange sculptural shapes

Brimham Rocks

Summerbridge, Harrogate,
North Yorkshire HG3 4DW

1970

Brimham Rocks, which offer panoramic views across Nidderdale and wider Yorkshire countryside, are an incredible collection of eye-catching rock formations. Sculpted by 320 million years of ice, wind and continental movement, these rocks have been moulded into magical shapes and have names such as the Dancing Bear and Druid's Writing Desk. It's a natural playground for those seeking adventure, but also offers tranquillity when exploring the surrounding moorland – with its rare wildlife habitat and internationally important plants. Brimham is a great place for walkers, climbers, nature-spotters and artists, as well as families looking for the freedom to explore. **Note**: nearest toilets 600 yards from car park.

Access: ⬚⬚⬚⬚⬚⬚

Find out more: 01423 780688 or brimhamrocks@nationaltrust.org.uk
nationaltrust.org.uk/brimham

East Riddlesden Hall

Bradford Road, Riddlesden, Keighley,
West Yorkshire BD20 5EL

1934

This hidden gem was saved from
demolition in 1934 and today offers a
friendly Yorkshire welcome to all who
pass through its 400-year-old doors.
The house and its history continue to
surprise us, as we unravel the stories
of ambition, success and failure of all
those who lived and worked here. The
intimate garden offers a relaxing space
all year. From fresh shoots in spring, to
cottage garden flowers in summer and
trees laden with fruit in autumn. The
natural play area, with mud-pie kitchen
and den-building corner, will spark the
imagination of the whole family.

Access:

Find out more: 01535 607075 or
eastriddlesden@nationaltrust.org.uk
nationaltrust.org.uk/east-riddlesden-hall

East Riddlesden Hall, West Yorkshire: saved from demolition in 1934, this hidden gem continues to surprise

Fountains Abbey and Studley Royal
Water Garden, North Yorkshire,
lie deep within the Skell Valley

Fountains Abbey and Studley Royal Water Garden

near Ripon, North Yorkshire HG4 3DY

1983

The playful 18th-century water garden

Deep within the Skell Valley lies Fountains Abbey and Studley Royal, a World Heritage Site waiting to be explored. Humans have tamed and teased the valley's wild waters over hundreds of years, creating an expansive landscape with sweeping Georgian water garden and imposing Abbey ruins. Cistercian monks chose this place to establish Fountains Abbey in 1132, and the walls echo with centuries-old stories. A riverside path leads to Studley Royal, a playful water garden designed by visionaries John and William Aislabie in the 18th century. Venture beyond the lake to Studley Royal deer park, with ancient tree avenues and red, fallow and sika deer.

Access:

Find out more: 01765 608888 or
fountainsabbey@nationaltrust.org.uk
nationaltrust.org.uk/fountains-abbey

Goddards House and Garden

27 Tadcaster Road, Dringhouses, York, North Yorkshire

1984

Meander through the Arts and Crafts garden 'rooms' of the former home of the Terry family (think Chocolate Orange). Discover fragrant borders and hidden corners or simply soak up the sunshine on the terrace. The Terry factory clock tower can be seen from the paddock orchard overlooking the racecourse.

Wisteria in the garden at Goddards, York

Satnav: enter 27 Tadcaster Road, Dringhouses, York, not postcode.

Access: 🅿♿🅿♿🚻

Find out more: 01904 771930 or
goddards@nationaltrust.org.uk
nationaltrust.org.uk/goddards

Productive greenhouse, above, and lawn, below, at Goddards House and Garden

Hardcastle Crags

near Hebden Bridge, West Yorkshire

1950 🏞♿

On an adventure at Hardcastle Crags, West Yorkshire

This picturesque valley has more than 25 miles of footpaths and 160 hectares (400 acres) of woodland to explore. You'll see tumbling streams, waterfalls, deep ravines and natural flood management interventions. It's home to the northern hairy wood ant and internationally rare waxcap grasslands. Seasonal highlights include sweet-smelling bluebells in late spring, carpets of golden leaves in autumn and rare, delicate frost flowers in winter. You can walk along the riverside to Gibson Mill, a former cotton mill and Edwardian entertainment emporium, where you'll find the café and can discover how the valley has changed over the past 200 years.

Spring bluebells at Hardcastle Crags

Note: steep paths, rough terrain. Toilets and café at Gibson Mill, 1 mile from car parks. **Satnav**: for Midgehole car park use HX7 7AA; Clough Hole car park HX7 7AZ.

Access: [icons]

Find out more: 01422 844518 (weekdays). 01422 846236 (weekends) or hardcastlecrags@nationaltrust.org.uk
nationaltrust.org.uk/hardcastle-crags

Maister House

160 High Street, Hull,
East Yorkshire HU1 1NL 1966

A merchant family's tale of fortune and tragedy is intertwined with the intriguing history of the 18th-century Maister House. **Note**: staircase and entrance hall only on show. Sorry no toilet.

Find out more: 01904 472027 (Beningbrough Hall) or maisterhouse@nationaltrust.org.uk
nationaltrust.org.uk/maister-house

Marsden Moor

near Huddersfield, West Yorkshire

1955 [icons]

This Site of Special Scientific Interest, with far-reaching views across the South Pennines and Peak District, has more than 2,000 hectares (5,500 acres) of countryside to explore. There's plenty of wildlife to spot, and recommended walks online will take you along miles of footpaths to favourite viewpoints. **Note**: sorry no toilet. **Satnav**: use HD7 6DH for the Information Room and Marsden village. HD3 3FT for Buckstones and HD9 4HW for Wessenden Head.

Find out more: 01484 847016 or marsdenmoor@nationaltrust.org.uk
nationaltrust.org.uk/marsden-moor

A view like no other at Marsden Moor, West Yorkshire

Middlethorpe Hall and Spa

Bishopthorpe Road, York,
North Yorkshire YO23 2GB

2008 🏚❓❓🎫

Middlethorpe Hall is a William III country house just outside York, built in 1699 and set in 8 hectares (20 acres) of gardens. Furnished with antiques and paintings, Middlethorpe retains the look and feel of a well-kept manor house. The bedrooms are complemented by elegant public rooms, including the drawing room and wood-panelled dining room, where imaginative meals are served. The gardens include a rose garden, walled garden, meadow and lake. The spa has a gym, swimming pool and sauna. **Note**: access is for guests staying at the hotel, using the spa or enjoying meals. Children over the age of six welcome.

Find out more: 01904 641241 or
info@middlethorpe.com
middlethorpe.com

Mount Grace Priory, House and Gardens

Staddle Bridge, Northallerton,
North Yorkshire DL6 3JG 1953

Explore the well-preserved ruins of a medieval priory, set in woodland with gardens and an Arts and Crafts manor house. **Note**: managed by English Heritage; Trust members free, except on event days.

Find out more: 01609 883494 or
mountgracepriory@nationaltrust.org.uk
nationaltrust.org.uk/mount-grace-priory

Nostell

Doncaster Road, Nostell, near Wakefield,
West Yorkshire WF4 1QE

1954 🏚✝❓🎫

A riot of colour at Nostell, West Yorkshire

Built to impress in the 18th century, Nostell is one of the great treasure houses in the north of England. Generations of the Winn family employed the best architects, craftsmen and artists to create a showcase for fashionable design. Discover interiors by influential architect Robert Adam, a world-class collection of furniture, textiles and wallpaper supplied by Thomas Chippendale, priceless paintings, a Georgian doll's house and a rare John Harrison clock. Home to wildlife including swans, kingfishers and bats, the surrounding 121-hectare (300-acre) estate includes parkland, lakes, a working kitchen garden and the tranquil Menagerie Garden. With displays of snowdrops, daffodils and bluebells, woodland cycle trails and all-weather paths, you can find new things to see and do in every season.

Access: 🅿♿❓♿♿❓

Find out more: 01924 863892 or
nostell@nationaltrust.org.uk
nationaltrust.org.uk/nostell

Watery fun on
a glorious autumn
day at Nostell

Exploring the grounds of Nunnington Hall in North Yorkshire, this picture, and discovering the welcoming house, below

Nunnington Hall

Nunnington, near York,
North Yorkshire YO62 5UY

1953

At this welcoming house and garden, in its beautiful setting on the River Rye, you can discover stories about the Fife family in the 1920s, as well as the rise and fall of Lord Preston during the 17th century. The organic garden is ideal for relaxing and you can picnic in the wildflower meadows and fruit orchards, while inside the house there is the Carlisle Collection of miniature rooms, renowned for its high-quality craftsmanship, to enjoy.

Access:

Find out more: 01439 748283 or
nunningtonhall@nationaltrust.org.uk
nationaltrust.org.uk/nunnington

Ormesby Hall

Ladgate Lane, Ormesby,
near Middlesbrough,
Redcar & Cleveland TS3 0SR

1962

A working estate on ancient farmland, this green space, with the Pennyman family home at its heart, is the last surviving historic estate in Middlesbrough. The Pennymans loved their garden and pleasure grounds, which now have newly opened vistas, a revived, colourful spring garden and a restored Victorian fernery. The 400-year-old estate has had many owners, from the scandalous Sir James Pennyman, the 6th Baronet, to the generous Ruth and Jim.

Discovering Ormesby Hall's fascinating past

Access:

Find out more: 01642 324188 or
ormesbyhall@nationaltrust.org.uk
nationaltrust.org.uk/ormesby-hall

Historic Ormesby Hall,
Redcar & Cleveland:
a valuable green oasis

Rievaulx Terrace

Rievaulx, Helmsley,
North Yorkshire YO62 5LJ

1972

Designed to impress, Rievaulx Terrace was created by the Duncombe family in the 18th century and is one of Yorkshire's finest examples of a landscape garden from this time. Peaceful woodlands, grand temples and a terrace with views of Rievaulx Abbey make this one of Ryedale's true gems. **Note**: no access from Rievaulx Terrace to Rievaulx Abbey (managed by English Heritage).

Access:

Find out more: 01439 798340 (summer). 01439 748283 (winter) or rievaulxterrace@nationaltrust.org.uk
nationaltrust.org.uk/rievaulx-terrace

Roseberry Topping

near Newton-under-Roseberry,
North Yorkshire 1985

Affectionately known as 'Yorkshire's Matterhorn', Roseberry Topping has woodland walks and wildlife on its slopes, and views from its summit. **Satnav**: use TS9 6QR.

Find out more: 0191 529 3161 or roseberrytopping@nationaltrust.org.uk
nationaltrust.org.uk/roseberry-topping

Treasurer's House, York

Minster Yard, York, North Yorkshire YO1 7JL

1930

Tucked behind York Minster, Treasurer's House is not as it first appears. In 1897 it was bought by Frank Green, the grandson of a wealthy industrialist, and by 1900 he had transformed it at great speed into an elaborately decorated town house, ready for the visit of Edward VII. Hear about Frank Green's life and find out how he saved Treasurer's House and changed it into the grand show home we see today. The award-winning garden is an oasis of calm, offering unrivalled views of York Minster, making it an ideal place to relax.

Access: ♿ 🚹

Find out more: 01904 624247 or
treasurershouse@nationaltrust.org.uk
nationaltrust.org.uk/treasurers-house-york

**Treasurer's House, York, North Yorkshire:
the tranquil grounds, below, and
grand interior, above**

Wentworth Castle Gardens

Park Drive, Stainborough, Barnsley,
South Yorkshire S75 3EN

2019 ♣ 🖼

Wentworth Castle Gardens, South Yorkshire

Working together with Barnsley Council
and Northern College, this estate, rooted
in rivalry, provides a space to bring people
together. Royal diplomat Thomas
Wentworth was outraged when a cousin
inherited his family home in 1695 and was
determined to outdo him, creating what
was once known as 'the finest garden in
England'. Today it is South Yorkshire's
only Grade I-listed landscape, with acres
of parkland and gardens to explore.
There are surprises along every avenue,
including a castle that is not what it seems.

Vibrant colour at Wentworth Castle Gardens

Note: house is closed to visitors as it houses Northern College.

Access: 🅿♿🚻♿♿

Find out more: 01226 323070 or wentworthcastlegardens@nationaltrust.org.uk **nationaltrust.org.uk/wentworth-castle-gardens**

Wentworth Woodhouse

Cortworth Lane, Wentworth, Rotherham, South Yorkshire S62 7TQ 2017

Large 18th-century country house, saved for the nation by Wentworth Woodhouse Preservation Trust, which is working to restore it. **Note**: house operated by Wentworth Woodhouse Preservation Trust. **Satnav**: use S62 7TQ.

Find out more: 01226 351161 or info@wentworthwoodhouse.org.uk

Yorkshire Coast

near Ravenscar, North Yorkshire

1976 🏛♿🚣‍♂️🚴‍♂️🐾

Yorkshire Coast, North Yorkshire: perfect weather for a day building sandcastles on the beach

The coastline from Saltburn to Filey has a rich heritage. Explore via clifftop walks or cycling routes, and discover sandy bays that are perfect for rock-pooling and fossil-hunting. Ravenscar Visitor Centre offers inspiring ideas for your visit, and there's a coastal exhibition at the Old Coastguard Station, Robin Hood's Bay. **Satnav**: for Ravenscar use YO13 0NE.

Access: 🚻

Find out more: 0191 529 3161 or yorkshirecoast@nationaltrust.org.uk **nationaltrust.org.uk/yorkshire-coast**

Yorkshire Dales

North Yorkshire

1946

The Yorkshire Dales is a great place to relax and explore the great outdoors. Take in the limestone landscape with its dry-stone walls and barns, fields of sheep and cows, and wildflower meadows and pastures. You can walk along the boardwalk at the National Nature Reserve at Malham Tarn and explore the river and woodland valleys of Upper Wharfedale on foot or by bike. Further north, Hudswell Woods has over 5 miles of footpaths through ancient woodlands, and there are peaceful spots along the River Swale to enjoy a picnic or perhaps skim a stone. **Note:** nearest toilets located at National Park Centre car parks or council car park (Hudswell Woods).

Exploring the Yorkshire Dales

Satnav: use BD23 5JA for Upper Wharfedale; BD24 9PT for Malham Tarn; DL10 4TJ for Hudswell Woods.

Access:

Find out more: 01729 830416 or yorkshiredales@nationaltrust.org.uk
nationaltrust.org.uk/yorkshire-dales

Yorkshire Dales, North Yorkshire: the River Swale offers many peaceful picnic spots

Following in ancient footsteps at
Hadrian's Wall and Housesteads Fort
in Northumberland

North East

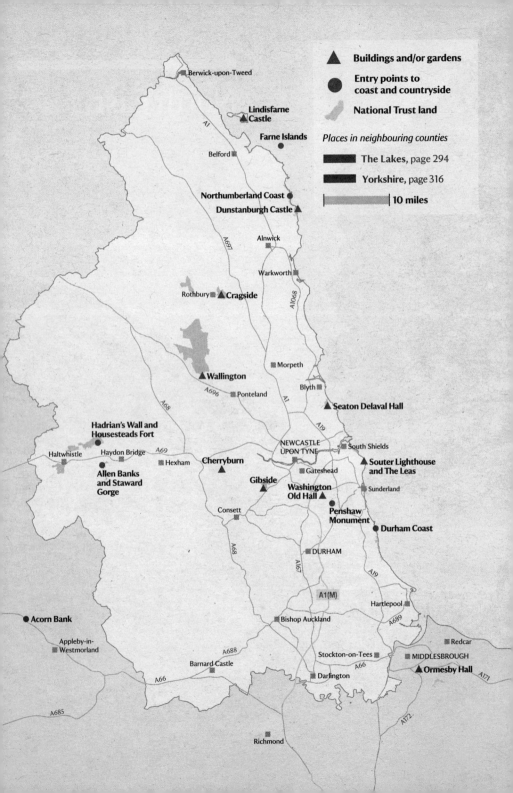

Places in neighbouring counties

The Lakes, page 294

Yorkshire, page 316

Buildings and/or gardens

Entry points to
coast and countryside

National Trust land

10 miles

Berwick-upon-Tweed

Lindisfarne
Castle

Farne Islands

Belford

Northumberland Coast

Dunstanburgh Castle

Alnwick

Warkworth

Rothbury

Cragside

Morpeth

Wallington

Ponteland

Blyth

Seaton Delaval Hall

A68

Hadrian's Wall and
Housesteads Fort

Haltwhistle

Haydon Bridge

Hexham

Cherryburn

NEWCASTLE
UPON TYNE

South Shields

Allen Banks
and Staward
Gorge

Gibside

Gateshead

Souter Lighthouse
and The Leas

Washington
Old Hall

Sunderland

Consett

Penshaw
Monument

Durham Coast

DURHAM

A1(M)

Hartlepool

Acorn Bank

Appleby-in-
Westmorland

Bishop Auckland

A689

Redcar

A688

Barnard Castle

Stockton-on-Tees

MIDDLESBROUGH

A66

Darlington

Ormesby Hall

A66

A685

Richmond

Allen Banks and Staward Gorge

near Ridley Hall, Bardon Mill, Hexham,
Northumberland NE47 7BP

1942

Dog-walking in the ancient woods at Allen Banks
and Staward Gorge in Northumberland

With its deep gorge created by the River
Allen, these ancient woods are the ideal
backdrop for an outdoor adventure and the
perfect place for nature lovers of all ages.
The semi-natural woodland is the largest in
Northumberland, with miles of waymarked
walks, sun-dappled paths and treetop
views. **Note**: due to severe storm damage
in 2015, parts of the site may be closed.
Satnav: postcode directs to Ridley Hall –
turn left at Ridley Hall gates for
Allen Banks car park.

Access:

Find out more: 01434 321888 or
allenbanks@nationaltrust.org.uk
nationaltrust.org.uk/allen-banks

Cherryburn

Station Bank, Mickley, Stocksfield,
Northumberland NE43 7DD

1991

Set in a tranquil garden with views
across the Tyne Valley, this unassuming
Northumbrian farmstead was the
birthplace of celebrated artist and
naturalist Thomas Bewick. Cherryburn is
still surrounded by the natural world that
inspired his work. Explore the museum with
Bewick's pioneering wood engravings and
meet the farm animals. **Satnav**: some
misdirect, follow brown signs.

Access:

Find out more: 01661 843276 or
cherryburn@nationaltrust.org.uk
nationaltrust.org.uk/cherryburn

The tranquil garden, below, and wooden type,
bottom, at Cherryburn, Northumberland

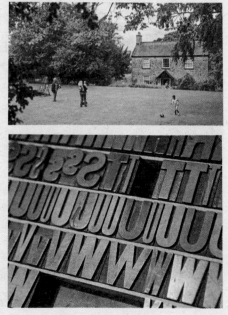

Cragside

Rothbury, Morpeth,
Northumberland NE65 7PX

1977 🏛 ❀ ♿

Trip the light fantastic to the home where modern living began. Cragside was the first house in the world to be lit by hydroelectricity, making it a wonder of the Victorian age. What started as a modest country retreat for engineer and inventor William Armstrong and his wife Margaret became the most technologically advanced house of its time with every home comfort imaginable, as well as being an Arts and Crafts masterpiece. Outside, Lord and Lady Armstrong were equally ambitious with the garden and grounds, engineering the landscape and experimenting with plants on a massive scale. Rocky crags, tumbling water, open lakes, towering North American conifers and great drifts of rhododendrons create changing scenery.

Cragside in Northumberland looks as rugged as the rocky crags it rises from

Intrepid young naturalists in the grounds of Cragside

Note: challenging terrain and distances outside, stout footwear essential.
Satnav: may try and bring you through exit. Please follow brown signs to main entrance.

Access: 🅿️🐕🚾🍴♿

Find out more: 01669 620333 or cragside@nationaltrust.org.uk
nationaltrust.org.uk/cragside

Dunstanburgh Castle

Craster, Alnwick,
Northumberland NE66 3TW 1961

This imposing castle ruin occupies a dramatic position on the Northumberland coastline, a mile from Craster, towering over Embleton Bay. **Note**: managed by English Heritage. Sorry no toilet – closest at Craster car park. **Satnav**: use NE66 3TT.

Find out more: 01665 576231 or dunstanburghcastle@nationaltrust.org.uk
nationaltrust.org.uk/dunstanburgh

Durham Coast

between Seaham and Horden,
County Durham

1987

Rocky headlands, sheltered bays, rare magnesian limestone grasslands and wildlife-rich wooded valleys characterise this coastline, part of Durham's Heritage Coast. The 'black beaches' of the coal-mining days have been cleaned up; clifftop paths look over a revitalised coastal landscape you can now explore.
Note: nearest toilets at Seaham.
Satnav: use SR7 7PS for Nose's Point car park (not National Trust) near Seaham.

Find out more: 0191 529 3161 or durhamcoast@nationaltrust.org.uk
nationaltrust.org.uk/durham-coast

A sheltered bay on the Durham Coast in County Durham

Farne Islands

Northumberland

1925 ✚ ⚓ 🐾

Farne Islands, Northumberland:
discover puffin heaven

Immerse yourself in nature. An exhilarating
boat trip takes you into the world of 23
seabird species during nesting season and
offers unrivalled close-ups of thousands of
puffins, Arctic terns and guillemots (May to
July). Each autumn, more than 2,000 grey
seal pups are born on the islands.
Note: Inner Farne island: basic toilets;
easy-access boardwalk. Staple Island:
sorry no toilet; challenging, slippery
terrain. Access by boat from Seahouses
(not National Trust), charge applies
(including members). Please show
membership cards at harbour trailer
(no facility to check membership validity).
Satnav: use NE68 7RQ.

Find out more: 01289 389244
(Lindisfarne Castle) or
farneislands@nationaltrust.org.uk
nationaltrust.org.uk/farne-islands

Gibside

near Rowlands Gill, Gateshead,
Tyne & Wear NE16 6BG

1974 ✚ ✿ ♿

A rare example of an 18th-century
landscape garden, Gibside was created
with spectacular views in mind. The vision
of coal magnate George Bowes and once
a pleasure ground for the Georgian elite,
this 290-hectare (720-acre) estate can
now be enjoyed by everyone. A tree-lined
avenue, Palladian chapel and orangery
sit among pockets of peaceful woodland.

**Three views of Gibside, Tyne & Wear, below
and opposite: once a Georgian pleasure ground**

The grand ruin of Gibside Hall offers a glimpse into the dramatic story of heiress Mary Eleanor Bowes. Adventure play areas and spotting wildlife, including otters and red kites, will keep families busy.

Access:

Find out more: 01207 541820 or gibside@nationaltrust.org.uk
nationaltrust.org.uk/gibside

Hadrian's Wall and Housesteads Fort

near Bardon Mill, Hexham, Northumberland NE47 6NN

1930

Hadrian's Wall and Housesteads Fort, Northumberland, is the best preserved Roman outpost in northern Europe

A UNESCO World Heritage Site, Hadrian's Wall is the Roman Empire's best preserved outpost in northern Europe. Sitting high within the dramatic landscape, this epic structure joins geology and human engineering. Follow ancient footsteps, exploring alongside the wall, and at the fort learn more about the soldiers' lives. **Note**: fort is National Trust-owned, English Heritage-managed and is a half-mile uphill walk from visitor centre. **Satnav**: can misdirect, please follow brown signs.

Access:

Find out more: 01434 344525 or housesteads@nationaltrust.org.uk
nationaltrust.org.uk/hadrians-wall

Lindisfarne Castle

Holy Island, Berwick-upon-Tweed,
Northumberland TD15 2SH

1944

Experience the magical feeling of
travelling across the causeway to
Lindisfarne Castle. Perched high on a
crag and commanding far-reaching views,
this iconic castle presides over Holy Island.
One of the UK's most recognisable
backdrops, it was converted from a fort
into a holiday home for the owner
of *Country Life* magazine by architect
Sir Edwin Lutyens in 1903. Beyond the
castle, you can explore the award-winning,
summer-flowering Gertrude Jekyll walled
garden and Victorian lime kilns and visit
the National Trust shop. **Note**: unfurnished
rooms. Limited toilet facilities. Island
accessed by tidal causeway – check
safe crossing times.

Access:

Find out more: 01289 389244 or
lindisfarne@nationaltrust.org.uk
nationaltrust.org.uk/lindisfarne

Iconic Lindisfarne Castle,
Northumberland, presides over Holy Island
and commands far-reaching views

Northumberland Coast

Northumberland

1935 [icons]

From Lindisfarne to Druridge Bay, you'll find wide open skies and miles of sandy beaches, teeming with wildlife. Coastal walks take you past dramatic castle ruins, unspoilt dunes and excellent rock pools. Spot seals, dolphins, wading shorebirds along the coast, and see the nesting shorebirds at Long Nanny shorebird site. **Note**: public car parks only (charge including members). **Satnav**: for Low Newton use NE66 3EH; Druridge Bay NE61 5EG; St Aidan's Dunes NE68 7SH.

Find out more: 01665 576874 or northumberlandcoast@nationaltrust.org.uk

Penshaw Monument

near Penshaw, Tyne & Wear DH4 7NJ 1939

This Wearside landmark can be seen from miles around. A sign of home for many, with woodland walks and views. **Note**: sorry no toilet. Walking routes nearby. **Satnav**: use DH4 7NJ.

Find out more: 0191 416 6879 or penshaw.monument@nationaltrust.org.uk
nationaltrust.org.uk/penshaw-monument

Seaton Delaval Hall

The Avenue, Seaton Sluice,
Northumberland NE26 4QR

2009 [icons]

Designed by Sir John Vanbrugh (Castle Howard, Blenheim Palace) and home to the flamboyant Delaval family, the Hall bears the scars of fierce fires which almost condemned it to ruin 200 years ago. In an age known for extremes of behaviour, the 'gay Delavals' were the most notorious of all Georgian partygoers and pranksters, whose dramatic personalities are matched by Vanbrugh's bold architecture. The Hall has

Seaton Delaval Hall in Northumberland: a place of parties and pranks

Souter Lighthouse and The Leas

Coast Road, Whitburn, Sunderland, Tyne & Wear SR6 7NH

1990

Breathe in the bracing North Sea air and climb all 76 steps to the top of the first lighthouse in the world designed and built to be lit by electricity. To the north stretches The Leas, with its wildflower meadows dotted with orchids. To the south is Whitburn Coastal Park, cared for by our rangers and great for wildlife – its nature reserve provides nesting sites, water and rest for migrating birds. The Engine Room and Keeper's Cottage give a flavour of life in a working lighthouse, while displays and exhibitions tell local stories.

Above and top, two views of the spectacular and dramatic gardens at Seaton Delaval Hall

recently undergone major conservation work and parts of the pleasure grounds have been renovated, creating a new Baroque theatre-inspired play area in the woodlands and a café in the Brewhouse.

Access:

Find out more: 0191 237 9100 or seatondelavalhall@nationaltrust.org.uk
nationaltrust.org.uk/seaton-delaval-hall

Souter Lighthouse and The Leas, Tyne & Wear: the crisp hoops, above, and rock-pooling, below

Note: Whitburn Coastal Park owned by South Tyneside Council, leased and managed by the National Trust.

Access: ♿♿♿♿♿

Find out more: 0191 529 3161 or souter@nationaltrust.org.uk
nationaltrust.org.uk/souter

Wallington

Cambo, near Morpeth,
Northumberland NE61 4AR

1941

A family-friendly wooded cycle trail at Wallington in Northumberland

Sitting in a rural corner of Northumberland yet only 20 miles north-west of Newcastle-upon-Tyne, Wallington is a large estate where a historic country house sits amid rolling hills, swathes of woodland and enchanting walled gardens. Take time to discover the variety of spaces, both indoors and out, and keep your eyes peeled for the native wildlife – from red squirrels and nuthatches, to white-clawed crayfish and otters. For an active adventure, take to the

Feeling completely at home at historic Wallington

Check opening dates and times before you set out: nationaltrust.org.uk

Washington Old Hall

The Avenue, Washington Village,
Washington, Tyne & Wear NE38 7LE

1956

The original Washington and medieval home of George Washington's ancestors. This small manor house has a diverse past, from its links to the first US President to a 17th-century home and even a crowded tenement. Discover tranquil gardens and explore the 'nuttery' – a haven for nature and wildlife.

Access:

Find out more: 0191 416 6879 or
washingtonoldhall@nationaltrust.org.uk
nationaltrust.org.uk/washington-old-hall

Medieval Washington Old Hall, Tyne & Wear, has links to the first US president

From autumn colours, top, to fresh spring blooms, above, there is something to enjoy every season at Wallington

Dragon Cycle Trail on two wheels and be inspired by far-reaching views across the Northumbrian countryside. Once home to the unconventional and socialist Trevelyan family, the informal house is full of treasured collections, while the three outdoor play parks capture the spirit of the adventurous Trevelyan children. **Note**: cycle hire charges apply (including members).

Access:

Find out more: 01670 773600 or
wallington@nationaltrust.org.uk
nationaltrust.org.uk/wallington

Sunny, spring day at Powis Castle and Garden, Powys

Cymru
Wales

Mae adran Cymru hefyd ar gael yn y Gymraeg. Os hoffech gael copi, gallwch lawrlwytho pdf yma: **nationaltrust.org.uk/handbook-welsh**

Gallwch hefyd e-bostio **wa.customerenquiries@ nationaltrust.org.uk** neu ysgrifennu at Swyddfa'r Ymddiriedolaeth Genedlaethol, Castell Penrhyn, Bangor, Gwynedd LL57 4HT

This Wales chapter is also available in Welsh. If you'd like a copy, you can download a pdf here: **nationaltrust.org.uk/handbook-welsh**

You can also email **wa.customerenquiries@ nationaltrust.org.uk** or write to the National Trust Hub Office, Penrhyn Castle, Bangor, Gwynedd LL57 4HT

Cemlyn

Holyhead

Penrhyn
Castle

Bodysgallen Hall

Llandudno

Conwy

Rhyl

LIVERPOOL

Beatles'
Childhood
Homes

Speke
Hall

A56

LLANGEFNI

A55

Conwy Suspension Bridge
Aberconwy House

CHESTER

Plas Newydd

Bangor

Bodnant Garden

A494

CAERNARFON

Ogwen Cottage

Segontium

Carneddau and Glyderau

A534

Hafod y Llan

Craflwyn and
Beddgelert

Tŷ Isaf

Tŷ Mawr Wybrnant

Wrexham

A5

Erddig

Porthdinllaen

Criccieth

Porthmadog

A525

Plas yn
Rhiw

Llanbedrog
Beach

Chirk Castle

Porthor

Abersoch

Dolmelynllyn
Estate

Oswestry

A495

A483

A49

A53

Porth Meudwy

A470

A494

A5

Shrewsbury

A442

Porth
y Swnt

Dinas Oleu

DOLGELLAU

A487

A458

WELSHPOOL

A458

M5

A489

A470

Powis Castle

Attingham
Park

Machynlleth

Newtown

A483

A458

A49

A487

A470

A483

ABERYSTWYTH

A44

Croft Castle

A456

LLANDRINDOD
WELLS

A44

Berrington
Hall

A44

A417

Llanerchaeron

Builth Wells

The Weir
Garden

A438

A438

Mwnt

Penbryn

Cardigan

Dolaucothi
Estate

Dolaucothi Mines

BRECON

A483

A470

A479

HEREFORD

A465

A49

Skenfrith
Castle

Cilgerran Castle

St David's
Visitor
Centre

A487

A40

Cwmdu

Paxton's
Tower

Dinefwr

Brecon
Beacons

A40

A470

Sugar Loaf
and Usk
Valley

The Kymin

M5

A40

Southwood
Estate

CARMARTHEN

A477

A40

A48

A483

Merthyr Tydfil

A4042

A49

A48

Martin's
Haven

Colby
Woodland
Garden

A4076

Llanelli

Aberdulais

Neath

Chepstow

Marloes
Sands
and Mere

Pembroke

Tudor
Merchant's
House

Llanelli

SWANSEA

Port Talbot

A470

Tredegar
House

NEWPORT

M48

Freshwater
West and
Gupton
Farm

Stackpole

Stackpole
Centre

Rhosili

Pennard,
Pwll Du and
Bishopston
Valley

M4

Bridgend

CARDIFF

M5

Dyffryn Gardens

M5

A38

A4

A37

▲ Buildings and/or gardens

● Entry points to
coast and countryside

National Trust land

H Historic House Hotel

Places in neighbouring counties

West Midlands, page 248

North West, page 276

⊢ 10 miles ⊣

To discover more
coastal and countryside
car parks in Wales, go to
nationaltrust.org.uk/
carparks

Aberconwy House

Castle Street, Conwy LL32 8AY

1934

This is the only medieval merchant's house in Conwy to have survived the turbulent history of the walled town over seven centuries. Its history includes a coffee shop, a temperance hotel and a bakery, as well as being a home for merchants and sea traders. **Note**: nearest toilets 50 yards. Steps to all parts of property.

Access:

Find out more: 01492 592246 or aberconwyhouse@nationaltrust.org.uk
nationaltrust.org.uk/aberconwy

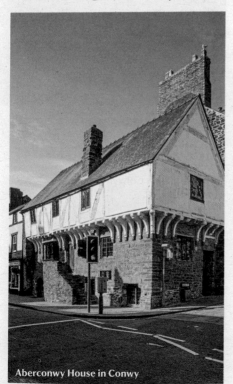

Aberconwy House in Conwy

Aberdulais

near Neath, Neath Port Talbot

1980

Exploring fascinating Aberdulais in Neath Port Talbot, top and above, one of Britain's earliest industrial sites

Aberdulais is one of the earliest industrial sites in Britain, a site where water has cascaded for centuries and innovation has harnessed its power. Water from the River Dulais and waterfall were powering industries long before the Industrial Revolution as Aberdulais established its place as a pioneering industrial centre.

Find out more on our website about how this small village in the Welsh valleys used cutting-edge technologies to shape the industries that changed the world; from tinplate to copper, Aberdulais played its part. **Satnav**: postcode misdirects, follow brown signs.

Access: 🅿️ 🅿️ ♿ 🚻 🎫 ♿

Find out more: 01639 636674 or
aberdulais@nationaltrust.org.uk
Aberdulais, near Neath,
Neath Port Talbot SA10 8EU
nationaltrust.org.uk/aberdulais

The immense power of water is apparent everywhere at Aberdulais

Bodnant Garden

Tal-y-Cafn, near Colwyn Bay,
Conwy LL28 5RE

| 1949 | 🏠 ✿ |

This Grade I-listed garden in Snowdonia's foothills, with historic plant collections and breathtaking mountain views, was established in 1874 by Victorian entrepreneur Henry Pochin. Five generations of the family have gone on to transform the 32-hectare (80-acre) Conwy Valley hillside with rare trees and shrubs from around the world. Since 1949 the garden has been nurtured in collaboration with the National Trust. You can enjoy Italianate terraces with

Bodnant Garden in Conwy, this page and left

Access: 🅿️♿ 🚻♿ 🐕♿

Find out more: 01492 650460 or
bodnantgarden@nationaltrust.org.uk
nationaltrust.org.uk/bodnant-garden

Bodysgallen Hall and Spa

The Royal Welsh Way, Llandudno,
Conwy LL30 1RS

2008 🏠❄️♨️

formal flowerbeds, pools and parterres,
informal shrub borders, woods, meadows
and riverside dells with waterfalls and
towering conifers. Every season brings
new delights – magnolias and
rhododendrons in spring, roses and water
lilies in summer, followed by rich leaf colour
in autumn and a stunning Winter Garden.
Note: steep paths and open water.

This Grade I-listed 17th-century house, set
within 89 hectares (220 acres) of parkland,
has the most spectacular views towards
Conwy Castle and Snowdonia. The
romantic gardens, which have won awards
for their restoration, include a rare parterre
filled with sweet-smelling herbs, as well as
several follies, a cascade, walled garden and
formal rose gardens. Beyond, the parkland
offers miles of stunning walks and views to
the coastline. **Note:** access is for paying
guests of the hotel, including for luncheon,
afternoon tea and dinner, and the spa.
Children over the age of six welcome.

Find out more: 01492 584466 or
info@bodysgallen.com
bodysgallen.com

The soaring peaks of the Brecon Beacons in Powys, offer the perfect challenge for hill-walkers

Brecon Beacons

Powys

1947 🏛🖼

The Brecon Beacons have captivated visitors for hundreds of years with their soaring peaks, including southern Britain's highest mountain, Pen y Fan. From the popular mountaintops to the tranquil valleys, lush farmland to ancient woodland, they are perfect for hill-walking and exploring. Not forgetting South Wales's highest waterfall, Henrhyd Falls, which plunges 90 feet into the wooded Graig Llech Gorge, a haven for rare mosses and ferns. In contrast, you can discover the vast remote moorlands of Abergwesyn Commons in the heart of Wales or ramble over the Begwns with panoramic views of the Brecon Beacons.

Find out more: 01874 625515 or brecon@nationaltrust.org.uk
nationaltrust.org.uk/brecon-beacons

Carneddau and Glyderau

Nant Ffrancon, Bethesda, Gwynedd

1951

This 8,498-hectare (21,000-acre) mountainous area includes Cwm Idwal National Nature Reserve, renowned for its geology and Arctic-Alpine plants, such as the rare Snowdon lily. There are nine tenanted upland farms here and nine peaks over 3,000 feet, including the famous Tryfan, where Edmund Hilary trained for his ascent of Everest. The area is home to a variety of wildlife, including otters, feral ponies and rare birds, such as ring ouzel and twite. The 60 miles of footpaths attract more than 500,000 walkers each year, while the bleak, photogenic landscapes have proved popular with artists.
Note: mountainous and difficult terrain – please come well equipped and check the weather. Charges apply in the National Park car parks. **Satnav**: use LL57 3LZ.

Find out more: 01248 605739 or carneddau@nationaltrust.org.uk
nationaltrust.org.uk/carneddau-and-glyderau

With 60 miles of footpaths, Carneddau and Glyderau in Gwynedd, this picture and above, is popular with hikers

Cemlyn

Anglesey

1971 ✝ 🖼 🏛 📷 ♿ 🚻 ♿ 🐦 🚶

Part of Anglesey's Area of Outstanding Natural Beauty, the north-west coast has a ruggedly beautiful coastline of rocks, small bays and headlands and is a delight for walkers. Cemlyn is a North Wales Wildlife Trust Nature Reserve and a Site of Special Scientific Interest. Renowned for its breeding colony of Sandwich, common and Arctic terns, Cemlyn Bay is a hive of seabird activity in spring and summer. Headland paths offer dramatic land and seascapes during autumn and winter. The brackish

Sea shells at Cemlyn

lagoon is separated from the sea by a remarkable shingle ridge. **Note**: nearest toilets in Cemaes Bay, 3 miles (not National Trust). **Satnav**: use LL67 0DY.

Find out more: 01248 714795 or cemlyn@nationaltrust.org.uk
nationaltrust.org.uk/cemlyn

The ruggedly beautiful coastline of Cemlyn, Anglesey, offers dramatic land and seascapes

Chirk Castle, Wrexham: as well as the awe-inspiring castle and prized gardens, visitors can explore the wilder grounds, below

Chirk Castle

Chirk, Wrexham LL14 5AF

1981 🏠🚶‍♀️♿✦♿♿✦

Completed by Marcher Lord Roger Mortimer in 1310, Chirk is the last Welsh castle from the reign of Edward I still inhabited today. You can explore medieval towers and dungeons, visit the 17th- and 18th-century rooms of the Myddelton family home, including the historic laundry, and discover the story of influential 20th-century tenant and polymath Lord Howard de Walden. The prized gardens contain clipped yews, herbaceous borders and rock gardens. A terrace gives stunning views over the Cheshire and Shropshire plains, while the large estate, divided by Offa's Dyke, provides habitat for rare invertebrates, wild flowers and veteran trees.

Access: ♿♿♿♿♿

Find out more: 01691 777701 or chirkcastle@nationaltrust.org.uk **nationaltrust.org.uk/chirk**

Cilgerran Castle

near Cardigan, Pembrokeshire SA43 2SF
1938

13th-century castle overlooking the Teifi Gorge – the perfect location to repel attackers. Walk the walls and admire the stunning views. **Note**: under the guardianship of Cadw – Welsh Government's historic environment service.

Find out more: 01239 621339 or cilgerrancastle@nationaltrust.org.uk **nationaltrust.org.uk/cilgerran-castle**

Colby Woodland Garden

near Amroth, Pembrokeshire SA67 8PP

1980

Young visitors at Colby Woodland Garden

A short walk from the beach, this hidden wooded valley, with its secret garden and industrial past, is a place for play. There are fallen trees to climb, rope swings and playful surprises everywhere. Spring brings bluebells, camellias, rhododendrons and azaleas, while the walled garden gives year-round colour, peace and seclusion. There are woodland walks, meandering streams and ponds with stepping stones and log bridges in the wildflower meadow, and the whole valley teems with wildlife.

Note: sorry, house not open.

Access:

Find out more: 01646 623110 or colby@nationaltrust.org.uk
nationaltrust.org.uk/colby-woodland-garden

Colby Woodland Garden, Pembrokeshire: this hidden valley, with its secret garden, is the perfect place to play

Conwy Suspension Bridge

Conwy LL32 8LD

1965

Conwy Suspension Bridge, Conwy: immense strength underlies the graceful design

Designed in the 1820s by Thomas Telford, this elegant suspension bridge with its restored tiny toll-keeper's house, stands beside Conwy Castle. Hidden between Stephenson's railway bridge and the modern road bridge, it has kept much of the original design and detailing its big brother, the Menai Suspension Bridge, has lost. **Note**: sorry no toilet.

Find out more: 01492 573282 or conwybridge@nationaltrust.org.uk
nationaltrust.org.uk/conwy-suspension-bridge

Craflwyn and Beddgelert

near Beddgelert, Gwynedd

1994

The 81-hectare (200-acre) Craflwyn Estate is set in the heart of beautiful Snowdonia, within a landscape steeped in history and legend. There's a network of paths and woodland walks to explore and tumbling waterfalls to discover. At Craflwyn you can learn about the princes of Gwynedd before venturing up to nearby Dinas Emrys, legendary birthplace of the red dragon of Wales. Within a couple of miles of Craflwyn, there are great walks for all abilities – from a village stroll at pretty Beddgelert to the rugged Fisherman's Path down the spectacular Aberglaslyn Pass. **Note**: sorry Craflwyn Hall is closed, although the public is welcome in the surrounding land.

Craflwyn and Beddgelert, Gwynedd: tumbling waterfalls

Rushing torrent at Craflwyn and Beddgelert

Satnav: use LL55 4NG.

Find out more: 01766 510120 or
craflwyn@nationaltrust.org.uk
nationaltrust.org.uk/beddgelert

Cwmdu

Llandeilo, Carmarthenshire 1991

Georgian terrace with pub, post office,
chapel and vestry. Representing a
rural Welsh village of the past.
Satnav: use SA19 7DY.

Find out more: 01558 685088 or
cwmdu@nationaltrust.org.uk

Dinas Oleu

near Barmouth, Gwynedd 1895

Mrs Fanny Talbot gave the Trust this
gorse-clad hill in 1895 – our first donation.
Note: steep rocky terrain and
steps to the top.

Find out more: 01341 440238 or
dinasoleu@nationaltrust.org.uk

Dinefwr

near Carmarthen, Carmarthenshire

1990

A special place in the heart of
Carmarthenshire, Dinefwr's historic
parkland is protected as a UK National
Nature Reserve. From flower-rich hay
meadows to dense ancient woodland,
it's all here for you to discover. The winding
driveway offers views of our rare-breed
White Park cattle, grazing the land as they
have done for 1,000 years. Newton House
is a relaxed, hands-on country house with
changing displays highlighting different
aspects of the property's history. Relax
in the garden, spot roaming deer, then
walk in the footsteps of ancient Welsh
princes to the castle.

**Newton House at Dinefwr,
Carmarthenshire**

Newton House, Dinefwr, is steeped in history

Note: Dinefwr Castle is owned by the Wildlife Trust and is under the guardianship of Cadw.
Satnav: enter Dinefwr, not postcode.

Access: 🅿️ 🅳 🆆🅲 🚹 ♿

Find out more: 01558 824512 or dinefwr@nationaltrust.org.uk
Llandeilo, near Carmarthen, Carmarthenshire SA19 6RT
nationaltrust.org.uk/dinefwr

Dolaucothi Estate Woodland

near Pumsaint, Llanwrda, Carmarthenshire 1944

Hours of woodland walks and multi-user trail with route information signage at the Gold Mines and Pumsaint village car parks.
Satnav: use SA19 8US.

Find out more: 01558 650809 or dolaucothi@nationaltrust.org.uk

Dolaucothi Gold Mines

Pumsaint, Llanwrda, Carmarthenshire SA19 8US

1941 📷 🏛️ ♿

Gold mines with centuries of stories dating back to Roman times surrounded by wonderful woodland walks. Take a guided tour of the only known Roman gold mine in Britain and see if you can spot signs of their gold-mining methods. From the car park at the gold mines, you can explore ancient woodland, wildflower meadows, mountain streams and upland pasture on our walks and multi-user trails.

Hard hats are needed for underground tours at Dolaucothi Gold Mines in Carmarthenshire

Note: steep slopes, stout footwear essential. Minimum height 1 metre. No carried children underground.

Access: ♿ ♿ ♿ ♿

Find out more: 01558 650809 (mines). 01558 650365 (caravan site) or dolaucothi@nationaltrust.org.uk
nationaltrust.org.uk/dolaucothi

From Victorian times to the 1930s, miners have endured the harsh working conditions at Dolaucothi Gold Mines, above and below

Dolmelynllyn Estate

Ganllwyd, Near Dolgellau, Gwynedd

1936 ♿♿

Evocative ruins at Dolmelynllyn Estate, Gwynedd

A 696-hectare (1,719-acre) estate, including woodland, two tenanted farms and Grade II-listed Dolmelynllyn Hall, with ornamental lake and parkland. There's a network of paths to explore with highlights which include the impressive Rhaeadr Ddu waterfall, ruins of Cefn Coch gold mines and wildlife-rich oak woodlands.
Note: Dolmelynllyn Hall is a privately run hotel, not a pay-to-enter property.
Satnav: use LL40 2TF.

Find out more: 01341 440238 or dolmelynllyn@nationaltrust.org.uk

Dyffryn Gardens

St Nicholas, Vale of Glamorgan CF5 6SU

2013 🏛️🔷

A garden for all seasons, Dyffryn is steadily undergoing restoration to its full Edwardian splendour. There is so much to discover. Winding paths lead to exquisitely designed garden rooms, grand lawns and an impressive arboretum. The walled gardens

Exquisite Dyffryn Gardens in the Vale of Glamorgan, above and below: are spectacular in all seasons

yield a bounty of fresh produce and the enormous glasshouse contains a striking collection of rare cacti and orchids. Designed by eminent landscape architect Thomas Mawson, the gardens are the early 20th-century vision of plantsman Reginald Cory. The huge wealth Reginald's father, John, had amassed with the family business, catapulted the Corys into high society. Their home, the Grade II*-listed Dyffryn House stands in the heart of the grounds.

Access: ♿️🅿️🚻♿️

Find out more: 02920 593328 or dyffryn@nationaltrust.org.uk
nationaltrust.org.uk/dyffryn-gardens

Dyffryn Gardens, above and below: among the best gardens in Wales

Erddig

near Wrexham, Wrexham

1973 🏛️✝️🏛️❄️😊♿️

Fully restored to its 18th-century glory, the garden at Erddig in Wrexham, above and right, delights all ages

A haven of natural beauty and modern sanctuary for wellbeing, Erddig's 485-hectare (1,200-acre) pleasure park, designed by William Emes, welcomes walkers (and their four-legged friends), beginner runners, Nordic walkers and those seeking a natural boost in the great outdoors. At its heart, above the River Clywedog, is the house – an unexpected survivor, rescued from dereliction in the 1970s. Discover the story of a family's unique relationship with its servants – a large collection of servants' portraits and carefully preserved rooms capture their lives across the generations, where saw and spade are as treasured as silver and silk. Outdoors, relax in a restored 18th-century walled garden with tranquil water features, trained fruit trees and apple orchards growing over 180 varieties. **Satnav**: do not use, follow brown signs.

Access: 🅿️♿️🚻♿️🎧♿️

Find out more: 01978 355314 or erddig@nationaltrust.org.uk
Erddig, near Wrexham, Wrexham LL13 0YT
nationaltrust.org.uk/erddig

Crashing waves and sandy fun, this picture and below, at Freshwater West, Pembrokeshire

Freshwater West and Gupton Farm

near Castlemartin, Pembrokeshire

1976

Freshwater West lies on a wild stretch of coast that's great for water sports and sandy adventures. Beyond the beach, you can discover Gupton Farm, our campsite, surf lodge accommodation and visitor hub. The perfect rustic escape for adventurous souls and nature lovers; go wildlife-watching, follow walking trails, make the most of the coast and pitch up on our campsite. **Satnav**: for Gupton Farm use SA71 5HW.

Access:

Find out more: 01646 623110 or freshwater@nationaltrust.org.uk
nationaltrust.org.uk/freshwater-west

Hafod y Llan

near Beddgelert, Gwynedd

1998

Set in the beautiful Nantgwynant Valley, Hafod y Llan is the largest farm run by the National Trust. Extending from the valley floor to the summit of Snowdon, part of the farm is designated a National Nature Reserve as well as a Site of Special Scientific Interest. Visitors are free to wander the many paths which cross this unique landscape. **Note**: this is a working farm, so access to the farmyard is on foot only. **Satnav**: use LL55 4NQ.

Find out more: 01766 890473 or hafodyllan@nationaltrust.org.uk

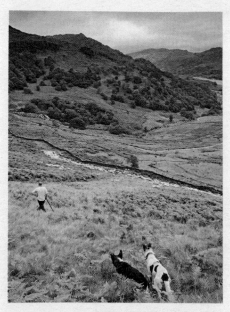

Hafod y Llan in Gwynedd, above and below, is the largest farm run by the National Trust

The Kymin

Monmouth, Monmouthshire NP25 3SF

1902

Enjoy panoramic views of the Brecon Beacons and Wye Valley; views that once delighted Lord Nelson and Lady Hamilton when they visited the Georgian banqueting house and Naval Temple in 1802. Although the Round House is not open, enjoy lovely walks in the woods and pleasure grounds, perfect for picnics. **Note**: sorry no toilet. Access to car park via steep winding single lane with passing places.

Access:

Find out more: 01874 625515 or kymin@nationaltrust.org.uk
nationaltrust.org.uk/kymin

The Kymin, Monmouthshire: panoramic views and plenty of space to picnic

Generations have enjoyed the golden sands of sheltered Llanbedrog Beach in Gwynedd, this picture and below

Llanbedrog Beach

Llanbedrog, Gwynedd

2000

This wonderful stretch of sand, best known for its colourful beach huts, has been enjoyed by generations. Its sheltered waters, fantastic views over Cardigan Bay and adjacent wooded and craggy landscape make this a real gem of Llŷn. **Note**: toilet (not National Trust). **Satnav**: use LL53 7TT.

Find out more: 01758 703810 or llanbedrog@nationaltrust.org.uk
nationaltrust.org.uk/llanbedrog-beach

Llanerchaeron

Ciliau Aeron, near Aberaeron,
Ceredigion SA48 8DG

1989

The walled garden at Llanerchaeron in Ceredigion

A self-sufficient 18th-century Welsh minor gentry estate. The villa, designed in the 1790s, is the most complete example of the early work of John Nash. It has its own service courtyard with dairy, laundry, brewery and salting house, giving a full 'upstairs, downstairs' experience. The walled kitchen gardens, pleasure grounds, ornamental lake, woodland and parkland offer peaceful walks, while the Home Farm complex has an impressive range of traditional, atmospheric outbuildings.

Marloes Sands and Mere

Marloes, Pembrokeshire

1941

A hidden gem on the western edge of Pembrokeshire, Marloes Sands beach is a long sandy stretch that is perfect for making a splash. Join us for a beach clean, spot marine life and go for a clifftop walk along the coast path. The wetland of

The garden at Llanerchaeron, top, and exploring the house, above

On the farm there are Llanwenog sheep and rare Welsh pigs, as well as chickens, geese and turkeys.

Access:

Find out more: 01545 570200 or llanerchaeron@nationaltrust.org.uk
nationaltrust.org.uk/llanerchaeron

Marloes Mere, just inland, is bustling with birdlife. Bring binoculars and get closer to nature at our on-site bird hides. **Note**: nearest toilets 164 yards along the track, just past Runwayskiln café and bunkhouse. **Satnav**: use SA62 3BH.

Access: 🚻

Find out more: 01646 623110 or marloessands@nationaltrust.org.uk
nationaltrust.org.uk/marloes-sands

Marloes Sands and Mere in Pembrokeshire: unrivalled views and plenty of chances to spot wildlife

Martin's Haven

near Marloes, Pembrokeshire

1981

This fabulously wild headland with fine panoramic views of St Bride's Bay is also the gateway to Skomer Island. For a really varied and exciting day, why not combine spotting marine wildlife with discovering traces of ancient settlements?

Martin's Haven, Pembrokeshire: seaside adventures

An irresistible path at Martin's Haven

Martin's Haven: a very special landscape

Note: nearest toilets by the slipway.
Satnav: use SA62 3BJ.

Access: ♿

Find out more: 01646 623110 or
martinshaven@nationaltrust.org.uk

Mwnt

near Cardigan, Ceredigion 1963

Beautiful secluded bay with a sandy beach –
perfect for spotting dolphins, seals and
other amazing wildlife. **Note**: steep steps
to beach. **Satnav**: use SA43 1QH.

Find out more: 01545 570200 or
mwnt@nationaltrust.org.uk
nationaltrust.org.uk/mwnt

Ogwen Cottage

Nant Ffrancon, Bethesda,
Gwynedd LL57 3LZ

2014 ⌾

Ogwen Cottage is nestled between
the dramatic Carneddau and Glyderau
mountain ranges, at the starting point for
numerous walking routes in the area. It
includes a base for our local ranger team
and outdoor education centre. This iconic
building has long been associated with
mountaineering and adventure, and there's
a range of rock-climbing and mountain-
walking routes nearby, as well as the
National Cycle Network's Lon Las Ogwen.

**Ogwen Cottage in Gwynedd has long been
associated with mountaineering and adventure**

Starting a walking adventure from Ogwen Cottage

Find out more: 01248 605739 or
ogwen@nationaltrust.org.uk
nationaltrust.org.uk/ogwen-cottage

Paxton's Tower

Llanarthne, near Dryslwyn,
Carmarthenshire 1965

Known as 'Golwg y Byd' (Eye of the World),
Paxton's Tower is said to offer views of
seven counties. **Note**: sorry no toilet.
Satnav: use SA32 8HX.

Find out more: 01558 823902 or
paxtonstower@nationaltrust.org.uk

Penbryn

near Sarnau, Cardigan, Ceredigion 1967

One of Ceredigion's best-kept secrets, this
beautifully secluded sandy cove lies down
leafy lanes, edged with flower-covered
banks. **Satnav**: use SA44 6QL.

Find out more: 01545 570200 or
penbryn@nationaltrust.org.uk
nationaltrust.org.uk/penbryn

Pennard, Pwll Du and Bishopston Valley

near Southgate, Swansea

1954

Spectacular cliffs, caves where mammoth
remains have been found, rare birds, an
underground river, bat roosts, silver-lead
mining, ancient woodland, smuggling and
limestone quarrying are just a few of the
wonders of this area. There are also
numerous archaeological features and two
important caves – Bacon Hole and Minchin
Hole. **Note**: due to dangerous rip tides,
swimming in Three Cliffs Bay is not advised.
Satnav: use SA3 2DH.

Access:

Find out more: 01792 390636 or
pennard@nationaltrust.org.uk
**nationaltrust.org.uk/pennard-pwll-du-
and-bishopston-valley**

Neo-Norman Penrhyn Castle and Garden in Gwynedd

Penrhyn Castle and Garden

Bangor, Gwynedd LL57 4HT

1951 🏠🏭✝⚙🖼

Penrhyn Castle is a vast neo-Norman castle with many different tales to tell. Set in 24 hectares (60 acres of gardens) and woodlands, it commands outstanding views across Snowdonia and the North Wales coast, perfect for walkers, runners and nature lovers. The Castle's dominating stone façade hides more than just its internal red-brick construction. Inside, the luxury of the exquisite carving and furnishings are deeply at odds with the links to slavery and bitter industrial dispute that changed Penrhyn's relationship with the local community for ever.

Access: 🅿️ ♿️ 🚻 🚶 ♿️

Find out more: 01248 353084 or penrhyncastle@nationaltrust.org.uk
nationaltrust.org.uk/penrhyn-castle

Plas Newydd House and Garden

Llanfairpwll, Anglesey LL61 6DQ

1976

Perfectly positioned on the shore of the Menai Strait with spectacular views of Snowdonia and Anglesey's coastline, Plas Newydd is surrounded by Grade I-listed gardens: the Italianate Terrace, Rhododendron Garden and an Australasian Arboretum. Transformed into a family

Plas Newydd House and Garden, Anglesey: the exterior and interior of the house, right top and bottom, and enjoying the garden, below

home by the 6th Marquess of Anglesey during the 1930s, it houses Rex Whistler's famous 58-foot mural and numerous works of art. You can discover more about the 1st Marquess and his military career and the life of the flamboyant 5th Marquess. Enjoy outdoor activities for all ages, including a hand-built treehouse, Frisbee™ golf course, adventure playground and the resident red squirrels.

Access:

Find out more: 01248 714795 or plasnewydd@nationaltrust.org.uk
nationaltrust.org.uk/plas-newydd

Beautiful 16th-century Plas yn Rhiw, Gwynedd, looks out across Cardigan Bay

Plas yn Rhiw

Rhiw, Pwllheli, Gwynedd LL53 8AB

1952 🏠 ✣ ♨

Standing on a hillside overlooking Cardigan Bay, Plas yn Rhiw is a beautiful 16th-century manor house with Georgian additions. The house was rescued from neglect and lovingly restored by the three Keating

sisters, who bought the property in 1938. The views from the grounds and gardens across the bay are among the most spectacular in Britain. The garden contains many beautiful flowering trees and shrubs, with beds framed by box hedges and grass paths – stunning whatever the season.

Access: 🅳 🅻 🎵

Find out more: 01758 780219 or plasynrhiw@nationaltrust.org.uk **nationaltrust.org.uk/plas-yn-rhiw**

Porth Meudwy

near Aberdaron, Gwynedd

1990

Nowhere expresses the essence of the area better than this sheltered cove on the wild and rocky coastline west of Aberdaron. It was from here that the pilgrims set out to Ynys Enlli (Bardsey Island). Today fishermen still bring the daily catch into the cove. Don't miss the unique Aberdaron boats: small wooden beach boats designed to dance nimbly through the waves along the craggy coastline. **Note**: sorry no toilet. **Satnav**: use LL53 8DA.

Find out more: 01758 703810 or porthmeudwy@nationaltrust.org.uk

The cove of Porth Meudwy in Gwynedd, above, is haven on this wild, rocky coastline, below

Porth y Swnt, above and below, in beautiful Aberdaron, Gwynedd: a visit of discovery and excitement

Porth y Swnt

Henfaes, Aberdaron, Pwllheli,
Gwynedd LL53 8BE

2010

This exciting interpretation centre, at the heart of the beautiful fishing village of Aberdaron, shines a light on Llŷn's unique culture, heritage and environment. You can experience the Bardsey Island lighthouse's retired optic up close, follow in the footsteps of pilgrims on a journey across the Sound in the video pod, catch up on what Llŷn's rangers are up to and form your reflective thoughts in the Sea of Words.

Access:

Find out more: 01758 703810 or
porthyswnt@nationaltrust.org.uk
nationaltrust.org.uk/porth-y-swnt

Porthdinllaen

Morfa Nefyn, Gwynedd

1994

This old fishing village really is a jewel. Perched on the end of a thin ribbon of land which stretches out into the Irish Sea, its clear sheltered waters lap against the stout stone houses. You can watch fishermen bring in the daily catch, while relaxing with a drink at the Tŷ Coch Inn. In the summer you can view the ecologically rich seagrasses from a paddle board – and have fun trying to stand up. **Note**: Porthdinllaen village is approximately 1 mile from nearest car park; no vehicle access. **Satnav**: use LL53 6DA.

Access:

Find out more: 01758 703810 or porthdinllaen@nationaltrust.org.uk
nationaltrust.org.uk/porthdinllaen

Picturesque Porthdinllaen, Gwynedd, sits at the end of a thin ribbon of land stretching out into the Irish Sea

Porthor

Aberdaron, Gwynedd

1981 ♿

This wonderful beach is famous for its 'whistling sands' and glistening waters. The whistling happens because of the especially fine sand grains on the beach – perfect for building sandcastles. If the joys of sandcastles and sunbathing are not enough for you, then why not have a go at surfing? The sea here is perfect. In addition, the Wales Coast Path runs in both directions from the car park. **Note**: nearest toilet in car park. **Satnav**: use LL53 8LG.

Access: ♿

Find out more: 01758 703810 or porthor@nationaltrust.org.uk
nationaltrust.org.uk/porthor

Perfect Porthor in Gwynedd, left and below

Imposing Powis Castle and Garden in Powys, above and below, offers a wealth of experiences

Powis Castle and Garden

Welshpool, Powys

1952

Once the stark medieval fortress of Welsh princes, Powis Castle was transformed over centuries into a grand home for the Herbert family, reflecting their wealth and status. Furnished with sumptuous fabrics, world-class artworks, furniture, tapestries and the unique Clive Collection of Indian and East Asian artefacts, the interior reflects the Elizabethan period through to the Edwardian period. With breathtaking

Powis Castle and Garden: plenty of space to roam

Rhosili and South Gower Coast

on the Gower Peninsula, Swansea

1933

The beach, above, and rugged clifftops, this picture, at Rhosili and South Gower Coast, Swansea

views across the Severn Valley, the garden is one of Britain's finest. Dating back more than 300 years, it includes 17th-century Italianate terraces lined with vibrant herbaceous borders and gigantic clipped yews, an Edwardian formal garden with century-old apple trees and rose beds, and a woodland area which boasts several champion trees. **Satnav**: postcode misdirects, enter Powis Castle.

Access:

Find out more: 01938 551920 or powiscastle@nationaltrust.org.uk
Welshpool, Powys SY21 8RF
nationaltrust.org.uk/powis

Lying at the far end of the beautiful Gower Peninsula, Rhosili is blessed with 3 miles of golden, award-winning sands and spectacular coastal views. It is the perfect base from which to explore the stunning South Gower coastline – most of which is in the care of the National Trust. From the historically and environmentally important medieval strip-farm system known as The Vile, the instantly recognisable Worm's Head tidal island, Iron Age earthworks, notable wildlife and geology, through to legends, shipwrecks and stories, there is so much to see. Once visited, Rhosili will stay with you for ever. **Note**: steep steps and a slope to the beach. **Satnav**: use SA3 1PR.

Access: ⬚⬚⬚

Find out more: 01792 390707 or rhosili@nationaltrust.org.uk
nationaltrust.org.uk/rhosili-and-south-gower-coast

St David's Visitor Centre and Shop

Captain's House, High Street, St David's, Pembrokeshire SA62 6SD

 1974

This visitor centre and well-stocked shop overlooks the Old Cross in the centre of St David's, Wales's smallest historic city. Why not take a look at our retail collection and then have a chat with one of the team about exploring Pembrokeshire (above)? **Note**: sorry no toilet.

Find out more: 01437 720385 or stdavidsshop@nationaltrust.org.uk
nationaltrust.org.uk/st-davids-visitor-centre

Segontium

Caernarfon, Gwynedd 1937

Fort built to defend the Roman Empire against rebellious tribes. **Note**: under the guardianship of Cadw – Welsh Government's historic environment service. Museum not National Trust. **Satnav**: use LL55 2LN.

Skenfrith Castle

Skenfrith, near Abergavenny, Monmouthshire NP7 8UH 1936

Remains of early 13th-century castle, built beside the River Monnow to command one of the main routes from England. **Note**: under the guardianship of Cadw – Welsh Government's historic environment service.

Find out more: 01874 625515 or skenfrithcastle@nationaltrust.org.uk **nationaltrust.org.uk/skenfrith**

Southwood Estate

Newgale, Roch, Pembrokeshire

2003

A timeless landscape of wooded valleys, floral fields and craggy cliffs, the Southwood Estate is full of scenic surprises. Follow the waymarked walking trails and explore the best of coast and countryside; spot flora and fauna and see how we're working hard to safeguard this special place. **Satnav**: for Southwood Farm car park use SA62 6AR; Maidenhall car park use SA62 6BD.

Two views of the scenic coastal path at Southwood Estate in Pembrokeshire

Access:

Find out more: 01646 623110 or southwoodestate@nationaltrust.org.uk **nationaltrust.org.uk/southwood-estate**

Stackpole

near Pembroke, Pembrokeshire

1976 🏠🏛️✿⚜️🏺🦅

A former grand estate stretching down to some of the most beautiful coastline in the world, including Broad Haven South, Barafundle Bay and Stackpole Quay. Today, Stackpole is a National Nature Reserve, recognised for its abundant flora and fauna; Bosherston Lakes are famous for their superb display of lilies and resident otters; and the dramatic cliffs of Stackpole Head are great for wildlife watching. You can uncover the history and heritage of this special place too; the former Stackpole Court site and nearby Lodge Park Woods reveal the story behind the magnificent designed landscape. **Satnav**: for Stackpole Quay use SA71 5LS; Broad Haven South SA71 5DR; Bosherston Lakes SA71 5DR; Stackpole Court SA71 5DE.

Access: 🅿️♿🚘

Find out more: 01646 623110 or stackpole@nationaltrust.org.uk **nationaltrust.org.uk/stackpole**

Stackpole, Pembrokeshire: the sandy beach at Broad Haven South, with distinctive Church Rock beyond

Runners enjoying the great outdoors, above and below, at Stackpole Centre in Pembrokeshire

Stackpole Centre

Old Home Farm Yard, Stackpole, near Pembroke, Pembrokeshire SA71 5DQ

1976

Located in the heart of the Stackpole Estate, our environmentally friendly Centre provides residents with easy access to Bosherston Lakes, Stackpole Quay and award-winning beaches – including Barafundle and Broad Haven South – as well as the historic site of Stackpole Court. The recently refurbished centre can house up to 147 guests and offers flexible accommodation with modern facilities, including a theatre, meeting and classroom space. It is ideal for groups, corporate clients, celebrations and family holidays.

Note: contact the centre for activity programmes, prices and availability.

Access:

Find out more: 01646 623110 or stackpolecentre@nationaltrust.org.uk
nationaltrust.org.uk/stackpole-centre

Sugar Loaf and Usk Valley

near Abergavenny, Monmouthshire

 1936

Sugar Loaf and Usk Valley in Monmouthshire

Discover glorious views across Monmouthshire and the borders from the peaks of Sugar Loaf and The Skirrid. Alternatively explore seasonal changes through the ancient woodland that straddles their slopes. By contrast, meander through parkland at Clytha and the Usk Valley, perfect for picnics or short walks. **Note**: sorry no toilet. Some car parks not National Trust (charge including members).

Find out more: 01874 625515 or sugarloaf@nationaltrust.org.uk **nationaltrust.org.uk/sugarloaf-and-usk-valley**

Tredegar House

Newport NP10 8YW

2012

Tredegar House and the Morgan family have been an important part of the Newport community for more than 500 years. Captivating tales of war heroism, inheritance disputes, Russian princesses and wide-ranging influence bring alive a home designed to impress and entertain. The modest but elegant contrasting formal gardens pay homage to life at Tredegar House.

A corner of the kitchen at Tredegar House in Newport

Tudor Merchant's House

Quay Hill, Tenby, Pembrokeshire SA70 7BX

1937 🏠

Over 500 years ago when Tenby was a busy trading port, a merchant built this three-storey house to live in and trade from. The building has been furnished with exquisitely carved replica furniture and brightly coloured wall-hangings which recreate the atmosphere of life in Tudor Tenby.
Note: sorry no toilet.

Access: ♿

Find out more: 01646 623110 or tudormerchantshouse@nationaltrust.org.uk
nationaltrust.org.uk/tudor-merchants-house

Tudor Merchant's House in Pembrokeshire

Exploring the extensive grounds, top, and the mirror-like lake, above, at Tredegar House

Satnav: please enter 'Pencarn Way' as well as the postcode.

Access: ♿ ♿ ♿ ♿

Find out more: 01633 815880 or tredegar@nationaltrust.org.uk
nationaltrust.org.uk/tredegar-house

Tŷ Isaf

Beddgelert, Gwynedd LL55 4YA

1985

Tŷ Isaf, Gwynedd, lies at the heart of pretty Beddgelert

Brimming with character, Tŷ Isaf is the oldest property in Beddgelert. You can see the front of this Grade II-listed late 17th-century building in the very heart of the village, and it has fulfilled many roles over the centuries – from tavern to farmhouse, to shop.

Find out more: 01766 510120 or tyisaf@nationaltrust.org.uk

Tŷ Mawr Wybrnant

Penmachno, Betws-y-Coed, Conwy LL25 0HJ

1951

Modest 16th-century farmhouse with huge cultural significance. Birthplace to Bishop William Morgan, whose 10-year endeavour to translate the Bible into Welsh helped ensure the survival of the language. The house is situated on the old drovers' road and there are several walking trails in the valley. **Note:** access via narrow road from

Characterful, but modest, Tŷ Mawr Wybrnant in Conwy has huge cultural significance

Penmachno. **Satnav**: do not use, follow brown signs instead. No access from A470.

Access:

Find out more: 01766 510120 or tymawrwybrnant@nationaltrust.org.uk
nationaltrust.org.uk/ty-mawr-wybrnant

Northern Ireland

The sun sets on the famous basalt columns at Giant's Causeway, County Antrim. Competition entry from Glenn Miles

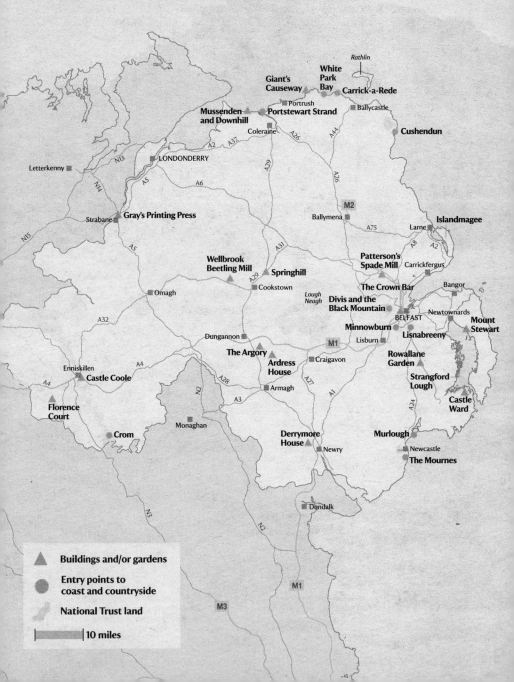

To discover more coastal and countryside
car parks in Northern Ireland, go to
nationaltrust.org.uk/carparks

Rathlin

Giant's
Causeway

White
Park
Bay

Carrick-a-Rede

Mussenden
and Downhill

Portrush

Portstewart Strand

Ballycastle

Cushendun

Coleraine

A2   A37

A26

A44

LONDONDERRY

Letterkenny

N13

A29

A26

N14

A5

A6

M2

Strabane

Gray's Printing Press

Ballymena

A75

Larne

Islandmagee

N15

A5

A8   A2

Wellbrook
Beetling Mill

A31

Patterson's
Spade Mill

Carrickfergus

Springhill

A29

Cookstown

Bangor

Omagh

Lough
Neagh

Divis and the
Black Mountain

The Crown Bar

Newtownards

A32

Minnowburn

BELFAST

Lisnabreeny

Mount
Stewart

Dungannon

M1

Lisburn

Enniskillen

The Argory

Craigavon

Rowallane
Garden

Castle Coole

A4

Ardress
House

Strangford
Lough

A4

A28

A27

A1

Castle
Ward

Florence
Court

N2

Armagh

A3

A24

Crom

Monaghan

Derrymore
House

Murlough

Newcastle

N3

Newry

The Mournes

N2

Dundalk

M1

M3

Buildings and/or gardens

Entry points to
coast and countryside

National Trust land

10 miles

Ardress House

64 Ardress Road, Annaghmore, Portadown,
County Armagh BT62 1SQ

1959

Blossom at Ardress House, County Armagh

Set within 40 hectares (100 acres) of rolling
countryside, this 17th-century farmhouse,
with detailed plasterwork and fine Georgian
interiors, offers afternoons of fun and
relaxation for everyone. The cobbled
farmyard is the perfect spot for children to
feed the resident chickens, and the nearby
apple orchards are great for exploring.

Access:

Find out more: 028 8778 4753 or
ardress@nationaltrust.org.uk
nationaltrust.org.uk/ardress-house

The Argory

144 Derrycaw Road, Moy, Dungannon,
County Armagh BT71 6NA

1979

This Irish gentry house can trace more than
190 years of history. Built in the 1820s for
the MacGeough Bond family, the house
and surrounding riverside estate came into
existence due to a quirky stipulation in a
will. The interior of this understated and
intimate house still evokes the eclectic
tastes and interests of the family. The small

The Argory in County Armagh

**Letting off steam on one of
The Argory's riverside wooded walks**

Exploring The Argory's understated interior, top, and the grounds in early autumn, above

rose garden with its unusual sundial, pleasure gardens and wooded walks along the River Blackwater are ideal for exploring.

Access: 🅿️🅳️🅱️

Find out more: 028 8778 4753 or argory@nationaltrust.org.uk
nationaltrust.org.uk/argory

Carrick-a-Rede

Ballintoy, County Antrim BT54 6LS

1967 🏷️🏷️

Connected to the cliffs by a rope bridge across the Atlantic Ocean, this rocky island is the ultimate clifftop experience. Jutting out from the Causeway Coastal Route, the 30-metre-deep and 20-metre-wide chasm separating Carrick-a-Rede from the mainland is traversed by an amazing rope

bridge that was traditionally erected by salmon fishermen. Wildlife-rich and with views across the seas to Rathlin Island, this is also home to Larrybane old quarry, featured in the television series *Game of Thrones*. **Note**: bridge access weather-dependent.

Access: [P♿] [♿WC]

Find out more: 028 2073 3335 or carrickarede@nationaltrust.org.uk
nationaltrust.org.uk/carrick-a-rede

Visitors brave the heart-stopping rope bridge at Carrick-a-Rede in County Antrim

Castle Coole

Enniskillen, County Fermanagh BT74 6HN

[1951] [🏛️♿]

Castle Coole in County Fermanagh: majestic Neo-classicism

Surrounded by a stunning landscape park, the majestic 18th-century home of the Earls of Belmore was created to impress. One of the finest examples of Neo-classical architecture in Ireland, the rooms at Castle Coole are brimming with opulence, luxury and colour. There are interesting pieces of history to explore, such as the servants' tunnel and ice house. The parkland,

Castle Ward

Strangford, Downpatrick,
County Down BT30 7LS

| 1953 | 🏠 🖼 🏛 🍴 ✿ ♿ 🚂 🐾 |

High on a hillside, with views across the tranquil waters of Strangford Lough, the Gothic and classical collide at Castle Ward. This eccentric 18th-century mansion within an extensive walled demesne, is one of the most peculiar architectural compromises between two people. In the farmyard, visit the water-powered corn mill, or stroll among flowers and subtropical plants in the newly restored Sunken Garden.

The tranquil waters of beautiful Strangford Lough at Castle Ward in County Down

There is plenty to entertain younger visitors at Castle Coole, both inside the house and out

interspersed with mature oaks, woodlands and paths, is perfect for refreshing walks, while the outdoor play area is great for families.

Access: 🅿 🚻 ♿ ♿

Find out more: 028 6632 2690 or
castlecoole@nationaltrust.org.uk
nationaltrust.org.uk/castle-coole

Castle Ward, above and right, offers two visits in one, with the classical-come-Gothic house – a most peculiar architectural compromise – and large, varied grounds

The laundry, tack room and dairy give an insight into life 'below stairs'. Discover more on the 21 miles of multi-use trails, while the woodland and adventure playgrounds and Secret Shore Nature Trail are great for children. **Note**: 1 March to 30 November, access to livestock grazing areas may be restricted.

Access:

Find out more: 028 4488 1204 or castleward@nationaltrust.org.uk
nationaltrust.org.uk/castle-ward

The historic ruins at Crom in County Fermanagh

Crom

Upper Lough Erne, Newtownbutler, County Fermanagh BT92 8AJ

1987

Home to islands, ancient woodland and historical ruins, this 800-hectare (2,000-acre) demesne sits in a tranquil landscape on the peaceful southern shores of Upper Lough Erne. One of Ireland's most important conservation areas, it has many rare species and is rich in wildlife, including fallow deer, red squirrels and pine martens.

Fun at Upper Lough Erne, Crom

An ideal spot for relaxing walks, cycling and boat trips. Visit the outbuildings, such as the summerhouse and boathouse. Jetty area available to use nearby. Turn your visit into a holiday with a stay in one of our holiday cottages (dog-friendly), award-winning glamping pods or campsites. **Note**: 19th-century castle not open to public.

Access:

Find out more: 028 6773 8118 or crom@nationaltrust.org.uk
nationaltrust.org.uk/crom

The Crown Bar

46 Great Victoria Street, Belfast, County Antrim BT2 7BA 1978

Belfast's most famous pub remains one of the finest examples of a high-Victorian gin palace complete with period features. **Note**: run by Mitchells & Butlers.

Find out more: 028 9024 3187 or info@crownbar.com
nationaltrust.org.uk/crown-bar

Cushendun

County Antrim

 1954

Peaceful Cushendun in County Antrim

Set at the mouth of the River Dun (Brown River) at the foot of Glendun, Cushendun is a very charming historic village steeped in character and folklore. The surrounding hills are a patchwork of farms, small fields, hedgerows and traditional stone walls. Sheltered harbour and beautiful beach. Views of Scotland. **Satnav**: use BT44 0PH.

Find out more: 028 7084 8728 or cushendun@nationaltrust.org.uk
nationaltrust.org.uk/cushendun

Derrymore House

Bessbrook, Newry,
County Armagh BT35 7EF 1953

Resting peacefully in a landscape demesne, this 18th-century thatched cottage is rich in history and a great place for walks.

Find out more: 028 8778 4753 or derrymore@nationaltrust.org.uk
nationaltrust.org.uk/derrymore-house

Divis and the Black Mountain

Hannahstown, near Belfast, County Antrim

2004

Sitting in the heart of the Belfast Hills, this 809-hectare (2,000-acre) mosaic of upland heath and blanket bog is a great place for a wild countryside experience. There are four walking trails to explore, affording panoramic views across Belfast and a wealth of flora, fauna and archaeological remains to discover. **Note**: cattle roam freely during summer months. Mountain environment and weather conditions can change rapidly. **Satnav**: use BT17 0NG.

Access:

Find out more: 028 9082 5434 or divis@nationaltrust.org.uk
nationaltrust.org.uk/divis

Divis and the Black Mountain, County Antrim

Florence Court

Enniskillen, County Fermanagh BT92 1DB

1954

Florence Court enjoys a majestic
countryside setting in West Fermanagh,
surrounded by lush parkland with
Benaughlin Mountain rising in the
background. There is something for
everyone to enjoy at this extensive and
welcoming place. Inside the Georgian
mansion you can hear stories about the
Earls of Enniskillen and their staff, who lived
here for more than 250 years. Outdoors
take a gentle walk or long cycle along
10 miles of trails in the adjoining forest
park and see fascinating industrial heritage
features, including the water-powered
sawmill and blacksmith's forge. The gardens
are home to the mother of all Irish yew
trees, as well as the kitchen garden, which
is being restored to its 1930s character.

Discovering the gardens at Florence Court

Access: P D 3 ♿

Find out more: 028 6634 8249 or
florencecourt@nationaltrust.org.uk
nationaltrust.org.uk/florence-court

Florence Court in County Fermanagh:
the Georgian mansion sits within lush parkland

Follow in the legendary footsteps of giants at Giant's Causeway in County Antrim

Giant's Causeway

44 Causeway Road, Bushmills,
County Antrim BT57 8SU

1962

Follow in the legendary footsteps of giants at Northern Ireland's iconic UNESCO World Heritage Site. The famous basalt columns of the Causeway landscape, left by volcanic eruptions 60 million years ago, are home to more than Finn McCool. Its nooks and crannies are dotted with dainty sea campion, and defensive fulmars protect their cliff nests. Windswept walking trails wind through this Area of Outstanding Natural Beauty, with an all-accessible walk at Runkerry Head and more challenging terrain along the Causeway Coast Way. The interactive exhibition and innovative audio-guides unlock secrets of the landscape and regale visitors with legends of giants.

Access:

Find out more: 028 2073 1855 or
giantscauseway@nationaltrust.org.uk
nationaltrust.org.uk/giants-causeway

Gray's Printing Press

49 Main Street, Strabane,
County Tyrone BT82 8AU 1966

The indelible story of printing is told behind
this Strabane Georgian shop front, once
reputed to be Ireland's printing capital.

Find out more: 028 8674 8210 or
grays@nationaltrust.org.uk
nationaltrust.org.uk/grays-printing-press

Islandmagee

near Larne, County Antrim 1996

An Area of Special Scientific Interest,
the peninsula at Islandmagee has some
of Northern Ireland's largest colonies of
cliff-nesting seabirds. **Note**: paths are
uneven and steep in places.
Satnav: use BT40 3TP.

Find out more: 028 9064 7787 or
islandmagee@nationaltrust.org.uk
nationaltrust.org.uk/islandmagee

Lisnabreeny

near Belfast, County Down 1938

On the edge of Belfast, paths through a
wooded glen cross farmland, emerging at a
rath on the Castlereagh Hills. **Note**: uneven
paths and steps. **Satnav**: use BT8 6SA.

Find out more: 028 9064 7787 or
lisnabreeny@nationaltrust.org.uk
nationaltrust.org.uk/lisnabreeny

Minnowburn

near Belfast, County Down

1952

The River Lagan at Minnowburn, County Down

Nestled in the heart of Lagan Valley
Regional Park, where meadows and
woodlands roll down to the River Lagan.
Perfect for a short stroll or longer walk.
Climb Terrace Hill to discover the garden
built by linen merchant Ned Robinson, and
stop for a picnic and to admire the views.
Note: trails are uneven and steep in places.
Satnav: use BT8 8LD.

Find out more: 028 9064 7787 or
minnowburn@nationaltrust.org.uk
nationaltrust.org.uk/minnowburn

Mount Stewart

Portaferry Road, Newtownards,
County Down BT22 2AD

1976

Voted one of the world's top 10 gardens,
Mount Stewart reflects a rich tapestry of
design and planting artistry bearing the
hallmark of its creator. Edith, Lady
Londonderry's passion for bold planting
schemes coupled with the mild climate
of Strangford Lough mean rare and tender
plants from across the globe thrive in this
celebrated garden, with the formal gardens
exuding a distinct character and appeal.

Mount Stewart, County Down: the elegant house and garden, below, and Strangford Lough, above

Exploring the lavish interiors of Mount Stewart, which have recently been restored to their full glory

Explore the exquisite house, recently restored to glory. Hear fascinating stories about the Londonderry family, and enjoy a world-class collection of paintings and many other internationally significant items. For a different view of Mount Stewart, stroll around miles of walking trails and discover a landscape lost in time.

Satnav: access via second gate into Mount Stewart, identified by brown sign.

Access: ⓟ ⓓ ⓦⓒ ♿ ♿ ♿

Find out more: 028 4278 8387 or mountstewart@nationaltrust.org.uk **nationaltrust.org.uk/mount-stewart**

The Mournes

near Newcastle, County Down

1992 🏛🏊🚶

These famous, wildlife-rich mountains are crossed by coastal and mountain paths. Great for exploring, the National Trust-maintained paths stretch from the shore into the heart of the Mournes, offering views over Dundrum Bay to the Isle of Man on a clear day. **Satnav**: use BT33 0EU for Slieve Donard and BT33 0LA for Bloody Bridge.

Find out more: 028 4375 1467 or mournes@nationaltrust.org.uk
nationaltrust.org.uk/mournes

The Mournes, County Down: a haven for wildlife

Murlough National Nature Reserve

near Dundrum, County Down

1967 🏛🏊🚶🐕

Two very different views of Murlough National Nature Reserve in County Down: a vital wildlife conservation site

Home to seals, Neolithic sites and Ireland's first nature reserve, Murlough is one of the most extensive examples of dune landscape in the country and an important wildlife conservation site. A network of paths and boardwalks winds through ancient dunes, woodland and heath, making the reserve ideal for relaxed walks and spotting wildlife.

Mussenden Temple and Downhill Demesne

Mussenden Road, Castlerock, County Londonderry BT51 4RP

1949 🏠🏛️🍴🌳🎭🏛️

Hezlett House at Mussenden Temple and Downhill Demesne in County Londonderry

The sheltered gardens, cliff-edge landmark and striking ruins of a grand headland mansion bear testament to the eccentricity of the Earl Bishop who once made this 18th-century demesne his home. Mussenden Temple, perched atop sheer cliffs, offers panoramic views of the famous north coast and is a great place for walking and kite-flying. Nearby at Hezlett House, life in a rural 17th-century cottage is told through the people who once lived there. One of the oldest thatched cottages left standing in Northern Ireland, it boasts a rare cruck frame and houses the Downhill Marble Collection.
Satnav: use BT51 4TW for Hezlett House.

Access: 🅿️♿

Find out more: 028 7084 8728 or mussendentemple@nationaltrust.org.uk
nationaltrust.org.uk/mussenden-temple

Watery fun, top, and discovering the coast, above, at Murlough National Nature Reserve

Note: limited toilet facilities with seasonal opening. **Satnav**: use BT33 0NQ.

Access: ♿

Find out more: 028 4375 1467 or murlough@nationaltrust.org.uk
nationaltrust.org.uk/murlough

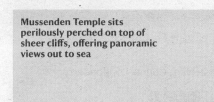

Mussenden Temple sits
perilously perched on top of
sheer cliffs, offering panoramic
views out to sea

Patterson's Spade Mill

751 Antrim Road, Templepatrick,
County Antrim BT39 0AP

1991 ⛏️🏭♿

Travel back in time and witness history
literally forged in steel at the last working
water-driven spade mill in daily use in
the British Isles. Dig up the history and
culture of the humble spade and discover
the origin of the phrase 'a face as long
as a Lurgan spade'.

Access: 🅿️🅳️🚻♿

Find out more: 028 9443 3619 or
pattersons@nationaltrust.org.uk
nationaltrust.org.uk/pattersons-spade-mill

The past comes to life
at Patterson's Spade Mill
in County Antrim

Portstewart Strand

Portstewart, County Londonderry

1981 🏭🏖️🚂🐾

There are two miles of golden
sand to enjoy at Portstewart
Strand in County Londonderry

Sweeping along the edge of the north
coast, this 2-mile stretch of golden sand is
one of Northern Ireland's finest beaches
and affords uninterrupted views of the
coastline. It's an ideal place for lazy picnics,
surfing and long walks into the wildlife-rich
sand dunes. **Satnav**: use BT55 7PG.

Access: 🅿️🚻

Find out more: 028 7083 6396 or
portstewart@nationaltrust.org.uk
nationaltrust.org.uk/portstewart-strand

Rowallane Garden

Saintfield, County Down BT24 7LH

1956 ❈

Carved into the County Down drumlin landscape since the mid-1860s, this inspirational 21-hectare (52-acre) garden is waiting to be discovered. The passion and shared vision of the Reverend John Moore, and later his nephew Hugh Armytage Moore, created a garden where you can leave the outside world behind and immerse yourself in nature's beauty. The formal and informal garden spaces are home to magical features mingled with native and exotic plants, such as drifts of rare rhododendrons. Follow in the

Glorious seasonal colours at Rowallane Garden in County Down, above and below

Inspirational Rowallane Garden, top and above, mixes native and exotic plants

footsteps of plant hunters and explore the sights and scents of their discoveries in the garden today.

Access: ⬚⬚⬚⬚

Find out more: 028 9751 0131 or rowallane@nationaltrust.org.uk
nationaltrust.org.uk/rowallane

Springhill

20 Springhill Road,
Moneymore, Magherafelt,
County Londonderry BT45 7NQ

1957 ⬚⬚⬚

Home to the Lenox-Conyngham family for 10 generations, this 17th-century plantation house is regarded as 'one of the prettiest houses in Ulster'. Hear the stories of this family home and discover the old laundry, which houses a celebrated costume collection that captures Springhill's enthralling past.

Spring flowers at Springhill, County Londonderry, below, and exploring the house, top right

Access: [icons]

Find out more: 028 8674 8210 or
springhill@nationaltrust.org.uk
nationaltrust.org.uk/springhill

Strangford Lough

County Down [1969]

The tidal treasures of the UK's largest
sea lough and one of Europe's key
wildlife habitats await discovery.
Satnav: use BT22 1RG.

Find out more: 028 4278 7769 or
strangford@nationaltrust.org.uk
nationaltrust.org.uk/strangford-lough

Wellbrook Beetling Mill

20 Wellbrook Road, Corkhill, Cookstown,
County Tyrone BT80 9RY [1968]

Discover how yarn was spun at
Northern Ireland's last working
water-powered linen beetling mill
and enjoy a woodland river walk.

Find out more: 028 8674 8210 or
wellbrook@nationaltrust.org.uk
nationaltrust.org.uk/wellbrook-beetling-mill

White Park Bay

near Ballintoy, County Antrim

[1939] [icons]

Embraced by ancient dunes and once home
to Neolithic settlements, this arc of white
sand nestles between two headlands on
the North Antrim coast. Home to a range
of rich habitats for a myriad of wildlife,
its secluded location makes it ideal for
quiet relaxation and peaceful walks.
Satnav: use BT54 6NH.

Access: [icon]

Find out more: 028 7084 8728 or
whiteparkbay@nationaltrust.org.uk
nationaltrust.org.uk/white-park-bay

**A tantalising glimpse of the arc of perfect sand
at White Park Bay in County Antrim**

Alphabetical index

Index

National Trust
Partner

Have you heard about National Trust Partners?
They are independent museums and heritage attractions that offer a special welcome to our members. This means you're entitled to a discount (in most cases, 50% off the standard entry price) when you show your National Trust membership card.

Most of these National Trust Partners are in London or Birmingham, and range from tiny specialist museums to the private homes of intriguing characters from history. But the list is ever-growing, so the best way to find out what's available now, and near you, is to head for our website and search for 'London partners' or 'Birmingham partners'.

Need to get in touch?

 enquiries@nationaltrust.org.uk

☐ nationaltrust.org.uk/help-centre

✉ PO Box 574, Manvers, Rotherham, S63 3FH

📞 0344 800 1895

0344 800 4410 (minicom)
9am to 5.30pm weekdays
9am to 4pm weekends and Bank Holidays.

 webchat

More useful links

Online shop
nationaltrust.org.uk/shop

Holidays
nationaltrust.org.uk/holidays

Historic House Hotels Ltd
historichousehotels.com

Royal Oak Foundation
royal-oak.org

National Trust for Scotland
nts.org.uk